EDMONTON
SCIENCE
FUN GUIDE

BARE BONES PUBLISHING

© 1997 Bare Bones Publishing

The Publisher
Bare Bones Publishing
Suite 355, 305-4625 Varsity Drive N.W.
Calgary, Alberta T3A 0Z9

Printed and bound in Canada by Webcom Limited.

Canadian Cataloguing in Publication Data
Main entry under title:
    Edmonton science fun guide

Includes index.
ISBN 1-896865-00-3
        1. Science—Alberta—Edmonton—Societies, etc.—Directories. 2. Science clubs—Alberta—Edmonton—Directories. 3. Science museums—Alberta—Edmonton—Directories. 4. Scientific recreations.

Q21.E35 1997   502'5'7123334   C96-900553-9

CONTENTS

ACKNOWLEDGEMENTS

Content
Jenny Glickman-Rynd
Loreen Jacobs
Linda Reynolds

Cover and Activity Illustrations
Joyce Harris

Production
Sika Patton
Linda Reynolds
Marvyl Stephenson

Financial support provided by Alberta Treasury Branches.
Donations also received from the Association of Professional Engineers Geologists and Geophysicists of Alberta (APEGGA), MTS Tectonics of Canada Ltd. and Webcom Limited.

We are also grateful to Beverley Cridland, Science Teacher, Rundle College, Calgary; Michael Caley, Co-ordinator, Edmonton Science and Technology Hotline; the Association for Bright Children—Edmonton Chapter; the Calgary Science Network and SCIENCE WORLD British Columbia for their inspiration and generous contributions to this project.

We would like to thank the following sources for permission to publish hands-on activities: Calgary Science Network, SCIENCE WORLD British Columbia, Alberta Agriculture Food and Rural Development, Alberta Environmental Protection, Education Section, Alberta Honey Producers, Aqualta, Association of Professional Engineers, Geologists and Geophysicists of Alberta (APEGGA), Bennett Environmental Education Centre, Canadian Red Cross Society, Children's Educational Wildlife Museum, Edmonton Power, Edmonton Reptile and Amphibian Society, Edmonton Science and Technology Hotline, Edmonton Space and Science Centre, Environment Canada, Strathcona Natural History Group, Telephone Historical Centre, Trout Unlimited, University of Alberta, Engineering Department (DiscoverE Science Camp) and the University of Alberta, Physics Department.

SCIENCE IS ABOUT US

How much science is in your everyday life? Think about it and you'll realize science and technology are everywhere. From the toothpaste you use to brush your teeth, to the bus you take to work or school, to the stove that cooks your dinner. Science is much more than mad geniuses mixing exploding chemicals in remote science labs—it's something that happens in your own life, every day.

Use the *Edmonton Science Fun Guide* to discover the scientist in yourself! Throw out the ideas of scientific stereotypes and realize that science is about **you**! Science is simply being curious, asking questions and having fun. We've included over 60 simple, fun activities for you to try at home or in the classroom, using inexpensive materials. These activities are designed to inspire curiosity and encourage you to delve further into the wonderful worlds of science and technology.

We have also included over 60 organizations in the Edmonton area that are involved in science and technology. Although the guide is not an exhaustive list of all science resources in Edmonton, it does reflect the wide range available. We have tried to choose groups with public profiles, and those that are open to inquiries. Because science is everywhere, we have not limited our selection to traditional sources, but have also included such groups as the Edmonton Symphony Orchestra, which features an excellent activity on the science of sound.

By trying hands-on activities, going for a walk in a park, or joining a computer club, you can connect science to your own daily life and open your eyes to how much science is about us. By taking science out of a text book and having you recreate it in your kitchens and classrooms, we believe your learning experience will be better and will stay with you much longer. We hope the *Edmonton Science Fun Guide* will likewise pique your curiosity about the science world around you.

HOW TO USE THIS GUIDE
We've organized the guide as follows:
- lefthand pages — Edmonton science and nature resources
- righthand pages — hands-on activities

Each hands-on activity is linked by topic to the Edmonton resource opposite it. In the index on page 147, the activities are linked to the Alberta Education elementary and junior high school science curriculum units. We hope teachers find this useful.

ALBERTA AGRICULTURE, FOOD AND RURAL DEVELOPMENT

WHO WE ARE
We are an Alberta government department, promoting and assisting agricultural development in the province.

Agriculture in the Classroom
Agricultural Education and Community Services Branch
Rural Development Division
2nd Floor, 7000 - 113 Street
Edmonton, AB   T6H 5T6

Tel: (403) 427-4225 or (403) 427-4311
Fax: (403) 422-7755

WHAT WE DO
We provide educational resource material, including print and multimedia, for educators, Grades 1 to 12. Our teacher handbooks show how agriculture is a diverse endeavour that affects urban Albertans. All materials are free.

Programs Offered
Preschool, elementary, junior high, high school, post-secondary credit, teacher training, community. **Field Trips:** Annual School Fair; call for details. **Summer Camps:** *Summer Agriculture Education Institute* for teachers. **Workshops/Special Programs:** Professional development for teachers (free resources).

Resources
Books, newsletter, teacher kits, slide shows, videos, films, information sheets and packages.

EARTHWORMS AND RAIN

WHAT YOU NEED

- 2 worm-ranch vivariums
- Aquarium gravel
- Sand
- Clay soil
- Topsoil
- Loose organic litter
- 20-40 live earthworms
- Water
- Timer

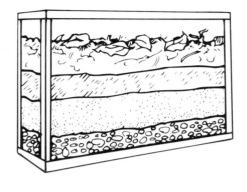

WHAT TO DO

1. Follow the diagram and set up the earthworm ranches on a tray.

2. Gently water your ranch until it begins to drain from the bottom of the frame onto the tray.

3. Place 20 earthworms on the surface, and wait a week.

4. Observe the earthworms' behaviour. When do they begin to move, to dig? What else are they doing?

5. Observe the worms for one week. What happens to the organic litter on the surface?

6. Pour water in the top of the vivarium, and soak until water drains out.

7. Note what changes occur and when. Be sure to note the time elapsed.

WHAT'S GOING ON?

Your vivarium acts like soil in the rain. You can observe the earthworms and their actions in the rain. You can also see how earthworms affect soil.

WHAT ELSE YOU CAN DO

When the water has stopped draining from the vivariums, put an incandescent light above them. What do the earthworms do?

ALBERTA BEEKEEPERS ASSOCIATION

WHO WE ARE
Our organization represents beekeepers and beekeeping within Alberta.

Alberta Beekeepers Association
16715 - 113 Avenue
Edmonton, AB   T5M 2X2

Tel: (403) 489-6949
Fax: (403) 487-8640

WHAT WE DO
The Alberta Beekeepers Association objectives are: (1) to promote, develop
and maintain good fellowship and co-operation among beekeepers; (2) to
propose, obtain and support government legislation; (3) to promote the
use of honey and other hive products; (4) to aid in the dissemination of
reliable and practical information about honey, bees and beekeeping.

Programs Offered
Although there are no formal educational programs, members are available
for classroom visits.

Resources
Teacher kits are available on request.

BEE WAGGLE DANCE

WHAT YOU NEED
- Nothing!

WHAT TO DO
1. Practise the two basic bee dances: the round and the waggle (see illustration). The patterns are related to each other, as you can see in the illustraion. Dance from the round into the waggle, and then back again.
2. Try the dances in a small space, then over a larger area. Is it more difficult to repeat the small or the large pattern?

WHAT'S GOING ON?
Bees perform the important function of pollination as they travel from flower to flower in search of nectar. Bees must make thousands of trips to flowers to make just one teaspoon of honey. Bee "dances" are a complex form of communication through which bees tell each other about the type and location of nectar supplies. If food is up to 10 m away, bees do the round dance. If food is more than 100 m away, bees do the waggle. Between 10 and 100 m, bees dance a combination of the two dances: the actual combination depending on the distance to the food. Bees also use the sun as a compass to indicate directions; they see the sun even on hazy days.

WHAT ELSE YOU CAN DO
Try group dances. Everyone forms a human chain and goes through the dance patterns together. Each person finds a partner. One partner chooses a spot as the location of some imaginary food. The objective is to then communicate to the other person, through a bee dance, the food's location.

ALBERTA BIRD RESCUE ASSOCIATION

WHO WE ARE
We are an organization providing rehabilitative care for injured wildlife.

Alberta Bird Rescue Association
51080 Range Road 223
Sherwood Park, AB   T8C 1G9

Tel: (403) 922-6103

WHAT WE DO
Through local veterinarians, we provide short- to long-term rehabilitative care for injured wildlife, with the intention of releasing the wildlife back to the wild.

Programs Offered
Elementary school, adult. Speakers are available for groups.

Resources
Teacher kits, portable exhibits, slide shows, videos, films, speakers.

FEEDING THE BIRDS

WHAT YOU NEED
- Large pine cones
- Suet
- Bird seed
- String

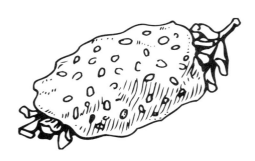

WHAT TO DO
1. Roll a pine cone in suet and then in bird seed.
2. Use string to suspend it from a branch outside for birds to eat. Be patient!

WHAT'S GOING ON?
While the birds will still find most of their food elsewhere, they will eventually recognize your pine-cone feeder as one of the many food sites they like to visit.

BE CAREFUL!
Hang your feeder away from where cats could reach the birds while they eat. In the fall and winter, once you start your pine-cone feeder, remember the birds will begin to rely on your source of food for them. Keep it well stocked.

Note: Don't use peanut butter instead of suet because it can make the birds' beaks stick together. They are then unable to feed at all, and can starve.

ALBERTA COLLEGE - COMPUTER CAMPS

WHO WE ARE
We are an educational institution, serving Albertans, which provides computer camps for school children in the summer months.

Alberta College
10050 MacDonald Drive
Edmonton, AB   T5J 2B7

Tel: (403) 428-1851
Fax: (403) 424-6371

WHAT WE DO
Call for a calendar of course offerings.

Programs Offered
Preschool, elementary, junior high, high school. Level I and Level II *Computer Camps for Kids* during July and August.

Resources
Books, information sheets, music lessons.

Facilities
Classroom, bookstore/giftstore, cafeteria, Muttart Hall (music recitals), computer labs.

MYSTERIOUS PAPER BAGS

WHAT YOU NEED
- 6 brown paper lunch bags
- Marbles
- Dimes
- Pen cap
- Cotton balls
- Paper clip
- Small erasers
- Tape
- Other small objects
- A few friends

WHAT TO DO
1. Without your friends seeing, label the bags with numbers and insert an object into each bag. Make notes for yourself of what's inside each bag.
2. Blow some air into each bag and seal it with tape.
3. List the objects that are in the bags on a separate piece of paper.
4. Have some friends take turns touching and moving the paper bags to figure out which object is inside.
5. Have your friends make a list of the objects they think are inside. They should keep their lists secret until everyone has had a turn.
6. When everyone has examined the bags, open them and compare the lists with the contents.

WHAT'S GOING ON?
The object of this demonstration is to show how scientists find out what is inside atoms. Because they cannot see into an atom, they have to figure it out by other methods.

WHAT ELSE YOU CAN DO
Try repeating this activity with items of similar sizes in the bags. Is it easier or more difficult to figure out what's inside?

ALBERTA COMMUNITY DEVELOPMENT
STEPPING STONES PROGRAM

WHO WE ARE

The Stepping Stones Program is offered by the Citizenship Services Branch of Alberta Community Development, a provincial government department.

Stepping Stones Program
Citizenship Services Branch
Alberta Community Development
Standard Life Centre
802, 10405 Jasper Avenue
Edmonton, AB   T5J 4R7

Tel: (403) 422-4927 or (403) 427-2927
Fax: (403) 422-6348

WHAT WE DO

The Stepping Stones Program promotes the idea that career choice is not a gender-linked decision and introduces the concept that every career is an option for women as well as men.

Programs Offered

Junior high, high school. This program is an optional resource to support the "Life Careers" component of the Grade 8 and 9 Health and Personal Life Skills curriculum and the "World of Work" theme of the Career and Life Management 20 curriculum. Many careers are profiled in Stepping Stones including research technician, chemist, forester, human genetics researcher, geophysicist, optometrist.

Resources

Teacher kits, information sheets, profile sets, research papers. The profile sets are interesting, "real life" stories of Alberta women working in non-traditional occupations. The profiles detail the women's work experience and feature on-the-job photographs and specific career information. Print materials are provided free of charge through Alberta Community Development.

MAKING A CRYSTAL CHEMICAL GARDEN

WHAT YOU NEED
- 90 mL salt
- 90 mL liquid blueing
- 15 mL ammonia
- An old pan
- Vaseline
- Pieces of coal or charcoal briquettes
- Food colouring

WHAT TO DO
1. Find an old pan and grease the edges with Vaseline (this prevents the mixture from going over the edge).
2. Place a few pieces of coal or charcoal briquettes in the pan.
3. Mix the salt, liquid blueing, and ammonia together.
4. Pour the salt mixture over the coal.
5. Dab drops of food colouring on top of the coal (you can use a variety of colours).
6. Watch your garden grow. Be patient! You should start to see crystals by the following day.

WHAT'S GOING ON?
The crystals are formed by salt molecules joining together as the liquid evaporates into the air. The ammonia helps to speed up the rate of evaporation.

WHAT ELSE YOU CAN DO
You can grow crystals of rock candy by dissolving sugar in boiling water. Pour the hot sugar water into a glass and dangle a piece of string from a pencil into the liquid. As the liquid cools, sugar crystals will appear.

BE CAREFUL!
If you are making the sugar crystals, be sure to get an adult's help, as hot water can be dangerous.

ALBERTA ENVIRONMENTAL PROTECTION EDUCATION SECTION

WHO WE ARE
We are a branch of Alberta Environmental Protection whose focus is educating the public on the issues relating to management and protection of Alberta's natural resources.

Alberta Environmental Protection
Education Section
9th Floor, South Petroleum Plaza
9915 - 108 Street
Edmonton, AB   T5K 2G8

Tel: (403) 427-6310
Orders:
Tel: (403) 422-2079
Fax: (403) 427-4402
World Wide Web: www.gov.ab.ca/~env/

WHAT WE DO
We provide environmental education resources and workshop services for schools, youth groups, communities and the general public. We also serve a role in supporting various events such as Wildlife Week, National Forest Week, Environment Week and Parks Day.

Programs Offered
Elementary, junior high, high school, teacher training, community, youth groups.

Resources
Teacher kits.

TRAPPING SOME AIR!

WHAT YOU NEED
- Spider plant (or any planted vine)
- A test tube or narrow jar
- Bowl
- Water

WHAT TO DO
1. Fill the test tube with water and cover the top with your thumb. Quickly put it upside down in a bowl of water.

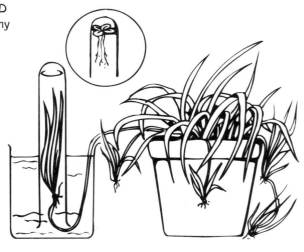

2. Gently place a runner of the plant into the test tube, making sure it stays under water.

3. Place the bowl in sunlight and wait a few hours. What do you see? Is the water level in the test tube lower?

4. Try this experiment in the dark. Do you see any difference?

WHAT'S GOING ON?
The bubble at the top of the test tube is oxygen gas. When you place the plant in the sun it uses water and sunlight to make food—this is called photosynthesis. During photosynthesis, plants produce oxygen, which we breathe. Plants are a particularly important part of our environment because of the oxygen they produce.

WHAT ELSE YOU CAN DO
Plants also make other kinds of gases. You may be surprised to know that yeast is a plant. Put 250 mL of *warm* water in a 2-litre plastic pop bottle. Add a package of yeast and some sugar. Spread some Vaseline on a cork and gently close the bottle. Wait, watch, and listen. The yeast makes carbon dioxide gas that makes the cork go POP!

ALBERTA ENVIRONMENTAL PROTECTION FISH AND WILDLIFE

WHO WE ARE
We are a provincial government department promoting sustainable, safe recreational use of Alberta's wildlife and natural habitats.

Alberta Environmental Protection Fish and Wildlife
Conservation Education Program
WISE Foundation
c/o 14515 - 122 Avenue
Edmonton, AB   T5L 2W4

Tel: (403) 427-3574
Fax: (403) 427-5695
World Wide Web: www.gov.ab.ca/~env/nrs/wildlife

WHAT WE DO
We offer workshops for individuals interested in the proper use of our resource kits. These certified instructors then work with their groups in the community: volunteer groups, school classes, clubs, etc.

Programs Offered
Programs are for Albertans of all ages. We co-ordinate three programs: *Conservation and Hunter Education, Fishing Education* and *Project Wild.*

Resources
Books, newsletter, presentations. All information is available to certified instructors free of charge. Manuals are for sale to the general public for a small fee at any Fish and Wildlife office in Alberta.

DINING OUT WITH TROUT

Note: Adult supervision is required for this activity.

WHAT YOU NEED
- A tin can of any size
- Cellophane
- 2 rubber bands
- Tape
- Plastic buckets
- Creek or small pond

WHAT TO DO
1. To make a viewer, remove both the top and bottom of a tin can. Make sure there are no sharp edges on the insides by using tape to cover them. Stretch a piece of cellophane or other clear plastic wrap over one end and secure it with a thick rubber band. The plastic must be stretched flat and the elastic tight to keep out the water. You may want to stretch a second elastic 1 to 2 cm above the first one, to secure the plastic even more, so it does not flop around.

2. At the edge of a creek or small pond, place the plastic end of the can under the water surface and look through the bare end. This tool helps to get rid of the reflection of light from the water's surface, so you will be able to see what goes on under the water.

3. Change the position of your viewer every two to three minutes to find out if location makes a difference to what you can see.

WHAT'S GOING ON?
Depending on the time of year, you should be able to see many aquatic or juvenile insects, fish and tadpoles.

WHAT ELSE YOU CAN DO
Bring ice-cream buckets and small plastic buckets and dip them into the water near the edges. Wait for the water to settle down and watch the insect life swimming around. Please put any creature you capture back in its home when you are finished looking.

BE CAREFUL!
Always remember to make sure that the place you are going to look is safe.

ALBERTA ENVIRONMENTAL PROTECTION
RECREATION AND PROTECTED AREAS

WHO WE ARE

We are a provincial government department, concerned with the administration of Alberta's protected areas.

Alberta Environmental Protection
Recreation and Protected Areas Division
8th Floor, Standard Life Centre
10405 Jasper Avenue
Edmonton, AB   T5J 3N4

Tel: (403) 427-7009
Fax: (403) 427-5980
World Wide Web: www.gov.ab.ca/~env/parks.html

WHAT WE DO

We provide environmental education information and hands-on opportunities at provincial parks. Many parks are suitable for day trips from Edmonton, including: Wabumun Lake, Hasse Lake, Strathcona Science Park, Cooking Lake Blackfoot Recreation Area, Miquelon Lake, Pigeon Lake, Pembina River and Ma-Me-O.

Programs Offered

Preschool, elementary, junior high, youth groups. Tours may be possible depending on site location. Workshops and special programs can be arranged on request.

Resources

Teacher resources, slide shows, videos, and films may be available on request.

Facilities

Interpretive/nature centre, live animals (not at all sites), trails.

MAKING A SOUND MAP

WHAT YOU NEED
- A large piece of paper or card
- A pencil crayon

WHAT TO DO
1. Choose a comfortable place to sit in your own backyard, at the beach or in a park. (This activity requires you to sit quietly for a while and listen to all the sounds around you.)

2. Take the piece of paper and draw an X in the middle of it. This shows where you are sitting.

3. Close your eyes and listen.

4. When you hear a sound, open your eyes and make a mark on the paper that represents the sound. For example, wavy lines might mean the wind; a jagged series of lines might mean a bird's call.

5. Make sure the position of the mark on the paper gives a true idea of the direction and distance of the sound.

WHAT'S GOING ON?
When scientists study noise levels, they might make sound maps. You have just made a sound map for your backyard, the beach or the park.

WHAT ELSE YOU CAN DO
Make a sound map at different times of the day. Compare the maps. What differences can you see? How many different sounds did you hear? Were there any sounds you had never heard before? Were there any sounds you could not identify?

ALBERTA HONEY PRODUCERS/WESTERN WAX WORKS

WHO WE ARE
We process, package and market honey. Western Wax Works processes, packages and markets craft, cosmetic, food and pharmaceutical wax.

Alberta Honey Producers/Western Wax Works
Box 3909, 70 Alberta Avenue
Spruce Grove, Alberta
T7X 3B1

Tel: (403) 962-5573
Fax: (403) 962-1653
E-mail: honey@beemaid.com
World Wide Web: www.beemaid.com

Days and Hours
Tours held Monday through Friday, 9:30 a.m. to 2:00 p.m.

Admission Fees
No admission fees for tours. Candle craft class $12.00 (includes supplies). School candle craft class $3.75 (includes supplies). Subsidies available.

WHAT WE DO
We promote the use of honey and wax through education and publicity.

Programs Offered
Preschool, elementary, junior high, youth groups, seniors, adults, family groups and teacher training. Groups of 20 to 50 adults, and groups of 15 to 30 children can be accommodated. Presentations on our company and bees. Videos available. Viewing windows of production area included in most tours, and honey tasting. Physical tours of the honey production floor are available to post-secondary groups. A candle craft class is available.

Resources
Books, information sheets, videos of beekeeping and honey and wax production. Display of hive and beekeeping equiment. Videos can be borrowed with a deposit. Our in-house video is for sale at cost.

Facilities
Classroom/science room, bookstore, giftshop.

LET THERE BEE LIGHT

WHAT YOU NEED
- Honeycomb - available at any craft store
- Wick
- A store bought candle
- Matches

WHAT TO DO
1. Place the wick at one end of the honeycomb.
2. Roll the honeycomb snugly around the wick. Do this in a warm room, or the honeycomb will be too stiff to roll smoothly and may crack.

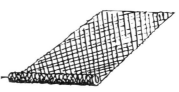

3. Set both your candles up in candle holders, and light them.
4. What do you notice about your honeycomb candle?

WHAT'S GOING ON?
We use many things that animals make. Wool comes from sheep. Eggs come from chickens. The wax in candles comes from bee honeycombs. Bees use the honeycomb in their hives as a place to store their honey, but honeycomb is made from wax, which burns very well.

Beeswax candles burn especially well, with almost no smoke. As well, the odour of burning beeswax is particularly pleasant, because bees make the honeycomb from the nectar of flowers.

WHAT ELSE YOU CAN DO
Look at the honeycomb. The structure of the honeycomb is particularly strong. It is made up of six-sided—or hexagonal—cells without any gaps or overlaps. It is tessellated. Only circles make stronger structures than hexagons, but if you tried to fit a large group of circles together you would have a problem. Try it. Cut out 20 or 30 equal size circles. Try to fit them together without any gaps or overlaps. Is it possible? Now do the same with hexagons. You can see why the honeycomb is a hexagonal tessellated structure.

BE CAREFUL!
Make sure you have help from an adult—matches can be dangerous.

ALBERTA MILK PRODUCERS

WHO WE ARE
Alberta Milk Producers represents Alberta's dairy farmers.

Alberta Milk Producers
14904 - 121A   Avenue
Edmonton, AB   T5V 1A3

Tel: (403) 453-5942
Toll free: 1-800-252-7530
Fax: (403) 455-2196
World Wide Web: www.amp.ab.ca

WHAT WE DO
We promote the use of milk through education and publicity. *CLUB MOO* is an educational and promotional program for elementary school children.

Programs Offered
Elementary, adults.

Resources
Teacher kits: *Milky Way* video and teaching resources on milk and the dairy industry. *CLUB MOO: Infopak* and *Fun & Games* are curriculum-related information and teaching ideas created each year.

CURDS AND WHEY

Note: Adult supervision is required for this activity.

WHAT YOU NEED

- Skim milk
- Vinegar
- Mixing bowl
- Spoon
- Strainer
- Wax paper
- Food colouring (optional)
- Fine weave cloth, about 30 cm x 30 cm

WHAT TO DO

1. With an adult's help, heat one cup of skim milk in a microwave or on the stove.
2. The milk should be very warm but not too hot. Colour the milk with a bit of food colouring if you like.
3. Pour the warm milk into the mixing bowl and add one tablespoon of vinegar. Stir gently with the spoon. The milk will curdle and separate into white (or coloured) blobs, and a cloudy liquid.

WHAT'S GOING ON?

You have just made the famous "curds and whey" of the nursery rhyme character, Little Miss Muffet. Milk is mostly water with calcium, some butterfat, protein, and some natural and added vitamins. The vinegar is a weak acid that reacts with the protein in the milk to turn it into solid curds. Most of the water is left behind as whey.

WHAT ELSE YOU CAN DO

Pour the mess of curds and whey into a cloth-lined strainer in the sink. Run a little water over the blobs in the cloth to wash the extra vinegar away. Pick up the corners of the cloth and gently squeeze out the remaining liquid. What you have is a lump of casein. It is most of the protein that was in the milk. Place it on wax paper to dry, or taste some of it. Isn't it like cottage cheese? With a little more processing, this casein can be used to make cheese, paint (see page 109), or even glue!

ALBERTA ORIENTEERING ASSOCIATION

WHO WE ARE
The Alberta Orienteering Association encourages, co-ordinates and administers orienteering as sport and recreation.

Alberta Orienteering Association
11759 Groat Road
Edmonton, AB   T5M 3K6

Tel: (403) 453-8577
Fax: (403) 453-8553

WHAT WE DO
The Alberta Orienteering Association provides opportunities for orienteering in Alberta at all levels of ability. Orienteering involves finding your way through terrain with the aid of map and compass. Participants navigate to different checkpoints marked on a map.

Programs Offered
Preschool, elementary, junior high, high school, adults, family, community, handicapped, senior citizens, youth groups. Regular meetings are hosted in the city and surrounding area. Beginners are welcome.

Resources
Books, newsletter, memberships, slide shows, videos, films, information sheets.

ON TRACK

WHAT YOU NEED
- Freshly fallen snow, or a muddy path
- A walk in a park
- Sketch pad and pencil
- Map of your local park (optional)

WHAT TO DO
1. Tracks made by people and animals can be easy to follow on a muddy pathway or on new snow. A great time to go for a walk in the park is after a snow fall. In your local park, practise following the tracks made by people and animals.
2. Look for bird and other wildlife tracks, even in your small neighbourhood park.
3. Draw the tracks on your sketch pad.
4. See if you can answer the following questions:

- In which direction was the animal going?
- In what order did the animal place its feet as it walked?
- What kind of animal do you think made the tracks?
- What do you think it could have been doing?

WHAT'S GOING ON?
Wild animals are often more active at night or when there are no people around to disturb them. Although we might not see the animals up close, we can find out what they were doing by looking at their tracks.

WHAT ELSE YOU CAN DO
When you can, go to a large park where you might find different kinds of animal tracks to draw. Take a map of the park, which you can probably get from your local City office. Mark on the map where you see the different animal tracks. Afterwards, take out a library book about animal tracks so you can compare the tracks you have seen and drawn with those in the book.

ALBERTA PLASTICS RECYCLING ASSOCIATION

WHO WE ARE
We are an Alberta not-for-profit organization dedicated to sustainable plastics recycling and to minimizing the amount of plastic waste that goes to the landfill.

Alberta Plastics Recycling Association
Room 102, 11720 Kingsway Avenue
Edmonton, AB   T5G 0X5

Tel: (403) 426-1493
Fax: (403) 424-4391

WHAT WE DO
The Alberta Plastics Recycling Association facilitates the development of efforts to manage waste plastic, and acts as a resource to individuals, groups and companies. The association is devoted to making Alberta a model of effective plastics waste management.

Programs Offered
Elementary, junior high school, community.

Resources
Newsletter, informational fact sheets, portable exhibits.

Facilities
Exhibits and displays.

SUNCATCHERS AND LIGHT

WHAT YOU NEED

- Clean, recycled Styrofoam trays
- Clear plastic transparency material
- Markers
- Glue or tape, string or yarn
- Scissors, sharp pencil, small cookie cutters

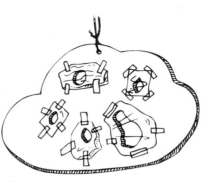

WHAT TO DO

1. Cut the edges off a Styrofoam tray so you have a flat surface.
2. Create openings in the tray with small cookie cutters, or by poking holes in a design shape using a sharp pencil.
3. Cut pieces of transparency material large enough to cover the openings, and colour the transparency pieces with markers.
4. Decide where you want to put the colours, and tape or glue the transparent material behind the openings in the tray.
5. Punch a hole near the top of the suncatcher and put a string or piece of yarn through and knot it.
6. Hang the suncatcher in a sunny spot or attach it to the window.

WHAT'S GOING ON?

White light from the sun is made up of different colours. When you look at a rainbow, you can see white sunlight broken up into a beautiful colour spectrum of red, orange, yellow, green, blue, indigo and violet. By using a filter like the pieces of coloured transparency that you cut, you can take colours out of white light. Filters allow only light of the same colour to pass through them. If you coloured your transparency blue, then only the blue part of white light can go through it. All the other colours are absorbed by the filter. This is how we see colours. When you look at a bright red rose, it is absorbing all of the colours from the sun **except** for red, which bounces off and reaches our eyes. In the evening, as sunlight fades, we see fewer and fewer colours.

WHAT ELSE YOU CAN DO

Put different coloured transparencies over the top of an existing one and discover what new colours are formed.

ALBERTA SOCIETY FOR INJURED BIRDS OF PREY

WHO WE ARE
We are a volunteer society of individuals concerned with the promotion and preservation of wild birds of prey.

Alberta Society for Injured Birds of Prey
51562 RR 222
Sherwood Park, AB   T8C 1H4

Tel: (403) 922-3024
Fax: (403) 922-3024

Days and Hours
Open to the public the third Wednesday of every month. Please phone ahead.

Admission Fees
Call for information.   Adults are free on school tours.

WHAT WE DO
We care for orphaned and injured wildlife and provide educational resources and opportunities for the public.

Programs Offered
Preschool, elementary, junior high, high school, adult, family, community, handicapped, senior citizens, youth groups. **Tours:** Group tours available for up to 30 people. Two- and three-day river trips, minimum of three people, maximum of eight, can also be organized. **Workshops:** *The Wildlife Rehabilitation Course* is offered annually in March. **Outreach:** A one-hour slide show on owls and the rehabilitation of an owl is available.

Resources
Newsletter, memberships, presentations, information sheets, portable exhibits, slide show.

Facilities
Exhibits and displays, live animals.

BEAK WATCHING

WHAT YOU NEED

- Different "beaks" (e.g., spoon, tweezers, clothespin, tongs)
- Food samples (e.g., small and large seeds, cereal, pasta shapes, marbles, foam chips)
- Stomach (e.g., a sandwich bag)

WHAT TO DO

1. Put the different types of food in different containers, e.g.:

    - seeds on a flat cookie sheet
    - marbles in a cereal bowl
    - foam chips in a bowl filled with water
    - pasta shapes on a tray
    - cereal in a shallow container filled with sand

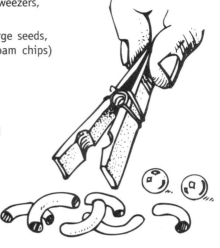

2. Try feeding yourself by using the different "beaks" to put the food in your stomach (the sandwich bag). Keep the bag at arm's length from the food source. Try not to get any sand or water in the bags.

3. Does one kind of beak work better than another? Is one beak better for a particular kind of food? Can you think of birds in nature that have beaks like the ones you used?

WHAT'S GOING ON?

A bird's beak can tell us a lot about its way of life. Birds of prey have hooked beaks for tearing flesh (bald eagles rip salmon open; golden eagles can tear the hide of dead sheep and hares). Wading birds have long, slender bills for probing in soft mud, where they find worms. Ducks have broad, flat bills that have a sieve inside for filtering tiny seeds from mud and water. Other birds have beaks designed for cracking hard nuts.

WHAT ELSE YOU CAN DO

The next time you're in a park or by the river, go bird watching. Have a look at the birds' beaks. Try to guess what kinds of food they eat and how they gather the food.

ALBERTA SOCIETY OF ENGINEERING TECHNOLOGISTS

WHO WE ARE

We are a professional society for applied science and engineering technicians and technologists.

Alberta Society of Engineering Technologists
2100 Canada Trust Tower
10104 - 103 Avenue
Edmonton, AB   T5J 0H8

Tel: (403) 425-0626
Fax: (403) 424-5053
World Wide Web: www.aset.worldgate.com

WHAT WE DO

We support and promote our profession through the certification of qualified applied science and engineering technicians and technologists. We promote quality education, and assist in the national accreditation of programs in Alberta's technical institutes and colleges. Volunteer speakers are eager to encourage students to pursue careers in science and technology, such as petroleum engineering technologist, chemical technologist, instrumentation engineering technologist and forestry technician, to name only a few!

Programs Offered

Junior high, high school, adult, youth groups.

Resources

Newsletter, presentations, videos, speakers, information brochures.

MARSHMALLOW HOUSE CHALLENGE

Your challenge is to design and build a structure that is strong enough to support a book, using only the materials provided.

WHAT YOU NEED

- Toothpicks
- Mini-marshmallows
- 2 books

WHAT TO DO

1. Build as big a free-standing structure as you can with 20 toothpicks and 10 marshmallows.

2. Try to have your structure support one book. Then try two books.

3. Try to build another structure with 30 toothpicks and 10 marshmallows (re-use the materials from your first structure). How many books will your second structure support?

WHAT'S GOING ON?

This challenge will give you a chance to try out different base shapes for a structure, as well as use some rather unique building materials. Think about which shapes are strong, and how these shapes can be combined to make a strong structure. Think about the shape of some bridges, furniture, houses, and other buildings, and think up some new shapes to try too!

ALBERTA UNDERWATER COUNCIL

WHO WE ARE
We are a group devoted to the science and recreation of underwater snorkelling and scuba diving.

Alberta Underwater Council
11759 Groat Road
Edmonton, AB   T5M 3K6

Tel: (403) 453-8566
Fax: (403) 453-8553

WHAT WE DO
We arrange snorkel and scuba diving outings at Alberta pools and lakes, as well as underwater hockey and rugby games. We practise and teach aquatic environmental protection and archaeology.

Programs Offered
Junior high, high school, adult, youth groups. Handicap-accessible programs are available only with advance notice and agreement. **Tours:** We conduct tours to archaeological sites as well as dive tours to approved locations.

Resources
Books, newsletter, memberships, slide shows, videos, films, magazines, information sheets, log books, maps.

CARTESIAN DIVER

WHAT YOU NEED
- A 2-litre plastic pop bottle with cap
- Water
- Glass medicine dropper
- Tall drinking glass

WHAT TO DO
1. Fill the drinking glass with water.
2. Fill the medicine dropper with enough water so it just barely sinks in the glass of water.
3. Squeeze the dropper and let a little bubble of air in. Now the dropper just barely floats.
4. Remove the label from the pop bottle.
5. Fill the pop bottle with water.
6. Carefully place the dropper in the pop bottle, without losing any water from the dropper.
7. Replace the cap tightly on the pop bottle.
8. Squeeze the sides of the sealed bottle really hard. What happens? Does the dropper sink to the bottom of the bottle? When you let go, what happens? Does the dropper rise to the top again?

WHAT'S GOING ON?
Squeezing the sides of the sealed pop bottle puts pressure on both the water and air inside the medicine dropper. The air inside the dropper is squeezed into a smaller bubble, which is then too small to make the medicine dropper float. When you stop squeezing the bottle, the air expands inside the dropper, and allows the dropper to float to the top again. Try the experiment again. Does the air bubble inside the medicine dropper change in size?

WHAT ELSE YOU CAN DO
Set up several medicine droppers to just barely float in the sealed pop bottle. As you slowly squeeze the sides of the bottle, the medicine droppers will sink to the bottom one after the other. Why? Why don't they all sink at once?

ALBERTA WHITEWATER ASSOCIATION

WHO WE ARE

We are an administrative body for decked canoeing and kayaking, with member clubs throughout the province. Each club provides services to its local area.

Alberta Whitewater Association
11759 Groat Road
Edmonton, AB   T5M 3K6

Tel: (403) 892-3390
Fax: (403) 892-4920

WHAT WE DO

We promote competitive and recreational river sports.

Programs Offered

Adult, family, community, youth groups. **Outreach:** Kayak instruction and kayak polo. **Workshops:** Winter pool lessons (handicap accessible at pool locations). **Summer Camps:** One-week kayaking camps available. Phone for details.

Resources

Newsletter, memberships, slide shows, videos, books.

H₂O ON THE GO

WHAT YOU NEED

- Aluminum foil pie plate
- Piece of string about 45 cm long
- Scissors
- Eraser
- Pencil
- Nut from a bolt (or other small weight)
- Tape
- Water source (e.g., faucet or hose)
- Ruler

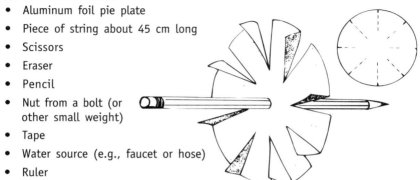

WHAT TO DO

1. Cut out the circular bottom of an aluminum foil pie plate. Make eight equally spaced cuts (dotted lines in illustration) toward the centre of the foil circle. End each cut about 2 cm from the centre.

2. Use a ruler to fold one edge of each section of the plate (see illustration) to make small ledges.

3. Punch a hole in the centre of the plate and push a pencil through it. The pencil should fit snugly in the hole; secure the pencil in place with tape.

4. Hold the wheel under a slow stream of water so that water hits the blades. Let the ends of the pencil rest lightly between your thumbs and index fingers. The wheel should turn smoothly.

5. Increase and reduce the flow of water. What happens to the wheel?

6. Tie one end of a piece of string to the pencil and attach a weight to the other end. The water wheel should wind the string, lifting the weight.

WHAT'S GOING ON?

Water power is based on water at a higher level having more "potential energy" (stored energy) than water at a lower level. When flowing from a high to a low level, water gives up some potential energy. This changes to "kinetic energy" (energy of motion) as the water falls. Moving water can turn a bladed wheel, transforming the kinetic energy into mechanical energy. In the past, mechanical energy from water wheels was used to grind grain and saw timber. Today moving water is used primarily in generating electricity. Power plants are built at the foot of high dams. Powerful jets of water shoot through pipes from a reservoir. The water hits the blades of dozens of water wheels, which turn electric generators.

ALBERTA WOMEN'S SCIENCE NETWORK (AWSN)

WHO WE ARE
Our mission statement: *To give women in science opportunities to realize their full potential and to attain a higher profile in society through visibility, networking and programs designed to fulfill these goals.*

Alberta Women's Science Network (AWSN)
P.O. Box 6912, Station D
Calgary, AB   T2P 2G1
(See below for Edmonton affiliates.)

Tel: (403) 282-6431
Fax: (403) 284-4750
World Wide Web: www.awsn.com

WHAT WE DO
The firm belief that education by example has a major impact on girls and young women, drives the mentor/role model programs. These programs are a key aspect of AWSN projects. Our speakers are eager to promote the pursuit of careers in math and science.

Programs Offered
Elementary, junior high, high school, post-secondary credit, teacher training, adult, community, handicapped, youth groups. Member organizations in Edmonton offering programs/presentations include:

Association of Women in Engineering and Science (AWES) (see page 48)
Tel: (403) 493-4681; Fax: (403) 493-4687
Speakers, Science Fair judges.

Women in Scholarship, Engineering, Science and Technology (WISEST)
Tel: (403) 492-1842
Choices — A one-day conference for girls in Grade 6. *SET* — A science, engineering and technology experience for students in Grades 9 to 12. *Summer Research Program* for post-Grade 11 students.

Resources
Books, newsletter, teacher kits, memberships, presentations, information sheets, conferences, reference catalogues, videos, guidebooks, resource files.

MÖBIUS STRIP

WHAT YOU NEED
- A long strip of paper
- Tape
- Crayons
- Scissors

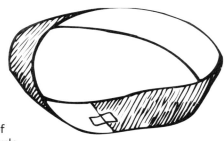

WHAT TO DO
1. Hold the two ends of the strip of paper together, as if to form a circle.
2. Without creasing the paper, give one end a half twist-turn.
3. Now tape the ends together.
4. Colour one side of the strip. What happens?
5. Follow one edge of the strip all around. What do you notice?

WHAT'S GOING ON?
This is called a Möbius strip. A Möbius strip has a surface with only one side and one edge.

WHAT ELSE YOU CAN DO
Find out what happens when you cut the band down the middle along its length. Predict what will happen when you cut a thin strip off one side of the band.

Take an old roll of wallpaper that has a pattern on one side. Make a Möbius strip big enough to walk in. Start walking forward on the patterned surface of the strip and follow it all the way round. (You might need to get a friend to hold up the strip while you walk.) What happens? What surface are you walking on? Patterned or plain?

AMATEUR RADIO STATION - VE6SSC

WHO WE ARE
We are an amateur radio station dedicated to introducing radio as a hobby.

Amateur Radio Station - VE6SSC
Edmonton Space & Science Centre
11211 - 142 Street
Edmonton, AB   T5M 4A1

Tel: (403) 452-9100
Fax: (403) 455-5882
E-mail: cssc@planet.eon.net

Meeting Place and Time
Saturdays, 8:30 a.m. to 11:30 a.m.

WHAT WE DO
Using the "state-of-the-art" Edmonton Space & Science Centre facilities, we are capable of providing worldwide communication on all amateur radio modes.

Programs Offered
Elementary, junior high, high school, adult, family, handicapped, senior citizen, youth groups.

Resources
Memberships, presentations, speakers, information sheets.

Facilities
Exhibits and displays, bookstore/giftshop, cafeteria/snack bar.

GOOD VIBRATIONS

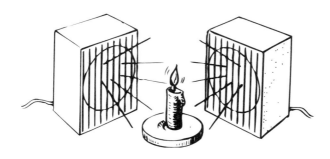

Note: Adult supervision is required for this activity.

WHAT YOU NEED
- Stereo system with two movable speakers
- Candle in a candle holder (and permission to light it!)
- Matches

WHAT TO DO
1. Put the two speakers about 30 cm apart.
2. Put the candle halfway between the speakers. Make sure the candle is not higher than the speakers.
3. Light the candle.
4. Now play some rock music—**loud**! Look at the flame.
5. Try changing the amount of bass and treble.
6. Try shifting the balance to one speaker and then the other. Watch the flame dance to the music.

WHAT'S GOING ON?
Sound moves in waves, like ripples on water. The sound waves from the speakers move through the air to hit the flame and make it vibrate.

WHAT ELSE YOU CAN DO
Lay one speaker on its side. Put a few grains of rice on the speaker and watch the rice dance.

BE CAREFUL!
Only light the match and candle with the permission and help of an adult.

AQUALTA

WHO WE ARE
We are the water company for the Edmonton area, supplying potable water to Edmonton-area households and businesses.

Aqualta
6th Floor, Capitol Square
10065 - Jasper Avenue
Edmonton, AB   T5J 3B1

Tel: (403) 412-3650
Fax: (403) 412-3013
World Wide Web: www.aqualta.com

Days and Hours
Tours and presentations available during the day. We can also accomodate groups after hours.

WHAT WE DO
We provide free educational services and materials to help Edmonton-area students learn more about water, its treatment and conservation, and watershed management.

Programs Offered
Elementary, junior high, high school, adult, youth groups. **Tours:** Conducted tours of the E.L. Smith water treatment plant are available. **Outreach:** Speakers are available to come to classrooms to discuss water issues. Free program topics include: water science experiments, water conservation, and water treatment presentations for elementary students.

Resources
Teacher kits, videos (*Water Follies, Water Works*), speakers, information sheets.

Facilities
Water treatment plant (tours only).

CLEAN UP YOUR WATER

WHAT YOU NEED
- 1 litre of water containing about 30 mL of dirt
- 3 glasses
- 300 mL soup can
- 150 mL clean sand
- 1 paper towel
- A hammer and nail

WHAT YOU DO
1. Label the three glasses A, B and C.
2. Shake up the container of dirty water.
3. Pour some of the dirty water into glass A.
4. Pour some into glass B and let it stand for 30 minutes without touching it.
5. Use the nail to punch small holes in the bottom of the soup can.
6. Line the can with the paper towel and fill it about halfway with sand.
7. Place the soup can over glass C. Fill the can with the remaining dirty water and watch it slowly filter into the glass.
8. Stir the water in glass A. Compare the water in the three glasses.

WHAT'S GOING ON?
The water in glass C is cleaned by the sand, which acts as a filter. The soil also acts like a giant filter to clean water. Water seeps through the soil to large underground storage areas, called aquifers. As polluted water seeps through the soil, dirt and sand particles trap many of the contaminants. Water treatment plants also filter out as many particles as possible.

WHAT ELSE YOU CAN DO
What happens if too many contaminants are trapped by your filter? What could you do to clean your filter if you had to use it more than once?

ASSOCIATION FOR BRIGHT CHILDREN—
EDMONTON CHAPTER

WHO WE ARE
We are a non-profit society providing information, support and advocacy for gifted and talented children and their families.

Association for Bright Children (ABC)—Edmonton Chapter
The Bright Site
6240 - 113 Street
Edmonton, AB   T6H 3L2

Tel: (403) 413-1630
Fax: (403) 413-1631

WHAT WE DO
Edmonton ABC works toward the goal of raising awareness of giftedness as an exceptionality, strives to maintain working relationships with Edmonton school districts, and provides information to the public. Membership offers the opportunity for networking and communication among parents of bright children.

Programs Offered
Preschool, elementary, junior high school, adult, family. Preschool group meets five or six times a year for field trips and activities. *Super Saturday* sessions (three a year) for children in Grades 1 to 6, cover a wide range of interests. *Discovery Group* targets Grades 5 to 9, meeting three or four times a year. *The Mentorship Network* matches children who have passionate interests, with mentors. ABC also sponsors adult education sessions several times a year.

Resources
Books, newsletter, memberships, videos, speakers, magazines, information sheets.

Facility
Resource room.

BOILING WATER IN A PAPER CUP

Note: Adult supervision is required for this activity.

WHAT YOU NEED
- Fireplace, barbecue or open fire pit
- Wood or other material for burning
- Paper cup (NOT made of waxed paper)
- Water

WHAT TO DO
1. Fill the paper cup three-quarters full of water. Place it on a stable surface in the fire area (or on the barbecue grill) **before the fire is lit**.
2. Build a fire (or light the barbecue). Soon the part of the paper cup above the water level will burn off, but the cup below the water level will stay intact.
3. When the temperature is hot enough, the water in (what is left of) the cup will boil, but the cup will not burn.

WHAT'S GOING ON?
The temperature necessary to ignite paper is far higher than needed to boil water. Although the fire is hot enough to ignite the paper cup, the heat energy is absorbed by the water, causing it to boil. Wherever water is in contact with the cup, the paper will not burn.

WHAT ELSE YOU CAN DO
If you continue to boil the water, the top edge of the cup will burn away as the water evaporates and the paper dries out. Do not try this on a stove with electric elements, but if you are very careful, it can be done over a gas stove.

BE CAREFUL!
This experiment **must** be done with an adult's supervision.

ASSOCIATION OF PROFESSIONAL ENGINEERS, GEOLOGISTS AND GEOPHYSICISTS OF ALBERTA (APEGGA)

WHO WE ARE

We serve society by regulating, enhancing and providing leadership in the practice of our member professions in Alberta. With more than 28,000 members, APEGGA is the largest professional association in the province. Our members use their expertise in areas as diverse as environmental technology, resource development, construction, public works, transportation, agriculture, manufacturing and forestry.

APEGGA
1500 Scotia Place, Tower One
10060 Jasper Avenue
Edmonton, AB   T5J 4A2

Tel: (403) 426-3990
Toll Free: 1-800-661-7020 (in Alberta)
Fax: (403) 426-1877
E-mail: email @apegga.com
Internet Home Page: http://www.apegga.com

WHAT WE DO

The association is one of the most proactive professional organizations in the province. Our volunteers keep young people informed of opportunities in science and technology, with an emphasis on how our professions impact the lives of Albertans.

Programs Offered

Elementary, junior high, senior high school. Volunteers present science demonstrations and promote science careers. Judges are available for science fairs. Student-oriented activities are offered each October during National Science & Technology Week. Each March, APEGGA sponsors the *Edmonton Science Olympics*.

CRAZY CANTILEVER BRIDGE

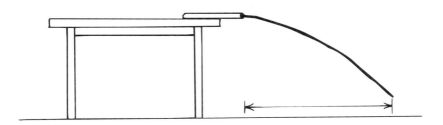

WHAT YOU NEED
- 30 pieces of uncooked spaghetti
- 35 cm of masking tape
- 1 paper towel tube
- Some friends
- A timer
- A table
- A tape measure

WHAT TO DO
1. Choose teams. You can have as many as five people in a team.
2. Set the timer for 25 minutes.
3. Tape the tube to the table with the end sticking out over the edge.
4. Build a cantilever bridge that is supported in the tube. Build the bridge as far out as you can. NOTE: You *can't* use any extra materials and the spaghetti can't touch the floor.
5. At the end of the time limit measure the distance from the table to the end of the bridge.

WHAT'S GOING ON?
Engineers have to work in teams all the time in order to design and build things. When you share ideas you are often able to build a much better bridge than if you try to work alone.

WHAT ELSE YOU CAN DO
Can you build a bridge or other structure using other things—like lasagna, or chopsticks?

ASSOCIATION OF WOMEN IN ENGINEERING AND SCIENCE (AWES)

WHO WE ARE
We are a group of women engineers and scientists in the Edmonton area.

Association of Women in Engineering and Science (AWES)
Edmonton Chapter
P.O. Box 1401, Edmonton Main
Edmonton, AB   T5J 2N5

Tel: (403) 998-8529
Fax: (403) 998-6723
World Wide Web: www.awsn.com

WHAT WE DO
Our mission is to give women engineers and scientists a higher profile in society by encouraging career advancement and to be visible role models for younger women. Our group meets monthly, alternating between personal and professional development topics and social events.

Programs Offered
Elementary, junior high, high school, adult, community, youth groups. Although we do not have any formal educational programs, some of our members are available for classroom visits. These include career presentations, science-curriculum enrichment and science-fair judging. In particular, we visit classrooms to show that women can have successful careers in traditionally male fields.

Resources
Brochures, regular/associate/student memberships.

MAGIC MUD

WHAT YOU NEED
- Cornstarch
- Bowl
- Water
- Spoon
- Pie plate
- Food colouring

WHAT TO DO
1. Empty the box of cornstarch into a large bowl and stir while you add water slowly. The "mud" should be as thick as icing so it's better to add too little water than too much.
2. Add a few drops of food colouring to finish the job.
3. Put your hands in the "goo"! What does it feel like? How does it act? What happens when you put some in your hand and press it? What happens after you stop pressing?

WHAT'S GOING ON?
Cornstarch and water make what is known as a suspension. It can act like a liquid, or, when pressed, like a solid.

WHAT ELSE YOU CAN DO
Pour some of the mixture into a pie plate. What happens when you smack your hand in the Magic Mud? Would water behave like that?

A messy time can be had by all!

BEAVERHILL LAKE NATURE CENTRE

WHO WE ARE
We are a facility at Beaverhill Lake promoting habitat preservation and birdwatching.

Beaverhill Lake Nature Centre
P.O. Box 30
5024 - 48 Avenue
Tofield, AB   T0B 4J0

Tel: (403) 662-3269
Nature Centre: (403) 662-3191
Fax: (403) 662-3929

Days and Hours
April through November, 8:00 a.m. to 6:00 p.m.

WHAT WE DO
We provide museum exhibits and guided tours of the surrounding nature trails.

Programs Offered
Preschool, elementary, junior high, high school, adult, family, community, handicapped, senior citizen, youth groups. **Tours:** Guided tours available for individuals or groups of 10 to 40 people. **Special Programs:** Beaverhill Lake Snow Goose Festival.

Resources
Books, memberships, presentations.

Facilities
Museum, exhibits and displays, interpretive nature centre, trails, bookstore/giftshop.

HUMBUG!

WHAT YOU NEED
- Paper cup or foam cup
- Piece of thin card
- Waxed paper
- Elastic band

WHAT TO DO
1. Use a cup and a piece of thin card to capture the insect you want.
2. Slide a piece of waxed paper between the cup and the cardboard, remove the cardboard and secure the waxed paper using an elastic band.
3. Hold the cup next to your ear. Can you hear the insect's wings beating? Do different insects sound alike or different?
4. Carefully release each insect once you have listened to it.

WHAT'S GOING ON?
The amplifier you made from the cup and wax paper increases the volume of the sound of an insect's wings beating. The beating wings cause the air in the amplifier chamber to vibrate; in turn, the air moves the waxed paper covering the cup. An insect that works particularly well in the chamber, and which is easy to catch, is the mosquito. A mosquito's wings flap 300 times per second. A honeybee's wings flap about 250 times per second. A fly's wings flap 190 times per second.

WHAT ELSE YOU CAN DO
Can you imitate the sounds you hear?

BENNETT ENVIRONMENTAL EDUCATION CENTRE

WHO WE ARE
We are an educational institution providing curriculum-based programs to teachers and their students.

Bennett Environmental Education Centre
Edmonton Public Schools
9703 - 94 Street
Edmonton, AB   T6C 3W1

Tel: (403) 468-1439
Fax: (403) 466-3370

Days and Hours
Day programs, 9:00 a.m. to 3:00 p.m.; overnight, throughout the year.

WHAT WE DO
We offer science-based activities and trips that supplement school science programs. Cost depends on group size and type of program.

Programs Offered
Elementary, junior high school, teacher training. **Field Trips:** *Building Things* for Grades 1, 3. *Owl Pellets, Pond Study, Pin-Hole Cameras, Discovering Trees and Forests, Adopt-a-Tree* and *Geo Day* for Grade 7. Other topics sometimes offered include: environmental activities, geology, geography and birds. **Outreach:** *Building Things* for Grade 3, *Building Things* for Grade 1, *Buoyancy* for Grade 2. **Summer Camp:** *Science Camp* for ages 10 through 12, in late August.

Resources
Resource kits available for groups and teachers when booking a program.

Facilities
Classroom, science room, trails.

FLAP LIKE A BIRD

WHAT YOU NEED
- Wingbeat chart
- Timepiece that indicates seconds
- A friend

WHAT TO DO
1. Bird's wings are like our arms. See how long you can flap your arms before they get tired.
2. Have your friend time you. Flap your "wings" for 10 seconds. Count the number of times you flap your wings.
3. Look at the wingbeat chart. Can you find a match?

   Did you flap your arms as fast as any bird flaps its wings?

WINGBEAT CHART

Bird	Wingbeats /10 Seconds
Crow	20
Robin	23
Pigeon	30
Starling	45
Chickadee	270
Humming Bird	700

WHAT'S GOING ON?
Some birds can fly as long as 48 hours, flapping their wings the whole way. People can't flap their arms that long. Birds are specially designed to fly. They have particularly well-developed chest (pectoral) muscles. Humans have stronger leg muscles because humans walk to move around.

WHAT ELSE YOU CAN DO
Take a look at the wingbeat chart. Choose a bird to imitate. See if you can flap your arms as fast as your bird. Can you figure out how often a humming bird flaps its wings in one minute?

CANADIAN CIRCUMPOLAR INSTITUTE

WHO WE ARE
We are an interdisciplinary research centre focusing on northern Canada and other circumpolar nations.

Canadian Circumpolar Institute (CCI)
University of Alberta
Old St. Stephen's College
3rd Floor, 8820 - 112 Street
Edmonton, AB   T6G 2E2

Tel: (403) 492-4512
Fax: (403) 492-1153

Days and Hours
Please call before visiting our library.

WHAT WE DO
Our mandate is to promote and support research on the circumpolar north, especially that involving interdisciplinary and multi-disciplinary programs. We foster communication among northern-oriented researchers and disseminate information. We can provide independent research, publication and extension services to university-based researchers, governments, industry and the general public.

Programs Offered
We offer presentations, seminars and workshops on request to preschool, elementary, junior high, high school, post-secondary credit, teacher training, adult, family, community, handicapped, senior citizen and youth groups.

Resources
Books, newsletter, teacher kits, slide shows, videos, films, magazines, information sheets, equipment.

Facilities
Library, bookstore.

CATCHING A BLOCK OF ICE

WHAT YOU NEED
- Piece of string about 15 cm long
- Salt
- Glass of cold water
- A few ice cubes

WHAT TO DO
1. Float the ice on the cold water in the glass.
2. Lay one end of the string on the ice cubes.
3. Sprinkle a little bit of salt on the string.
4. Count slowly to 10.
5. Gently lift the string.

WHAT'S GOING ON?
Usually water freezes at 0°C, but water with salt in it doesn't freeze until it is colder than 0°C. So, when you add salt to the ice, it melts. But when ordinary water from the glass is added to the little pool of salty water, it refreezes and traps the string.

WHAT ELSE YOU CAN DO
Put a glass that is very full of water in the freezer. What happens when the water freezes?

CANADIAN INDUSTRIAL INNOVATION CENTRE

WHO WE ARE

We originated at the University of Waterloo in 1976 and are currently a not-for-profit organization partially funded by the Federal Department of Industry, Canada. We assist inventors, entrepreneurs and educators across Canada.

Canadian Industrial Innovation Centre
156 Columbia Street West
Waterloo, ON   N2L 3L3

Toll free: 1-800-265-4559
Fax: (519) 885-5729

WHAT WE DO

The Innovation Centre has evaluated over 15,000 Canadian product ideas through the *Inventor's Assistance Program*. Other services include: market research, engineering, seminars for inventors, workshops for educators and classroom presentations.

Programs Offered

Public workshops, classroom visits and *Train the Trainers,* a workshop for teachers looking for assistance implementing innovation into their curriculum.

Resources

Newsletter (*Eureka!*); catalogue of over 200 books, tapes and software on innovation, creativity and entrepreneurship.

MODEL FIRE EXTINGUISHER

WHAT YOU NEED

- 375 mL plastic or glass bottle with a screw cap or cork
- Drinking straw (flex-straw)
- Plasticine
- Paper clip
- Thread
- Two-ply toilet paper
- Baking soda
- Vinegar
- Water

WHAT TO DO

1. Drill a hole through the bottle cap or cork just large enough to let the straw pass through it.

2. Push the straw through the cap so that the long part will be inside the bottle. Seal the straw to the cap with Plasticine to make it an airtight seal.

3. Pour about 100 mL of vinegar into the bottle and add water until the bottle is three-quarters full.

4. Separate the two thicknesses of a piece of toilet paper to create one very thin sheet of paper.

5. Using the sheet of paper made in Step 4, make a narrow bag tied at the top with about 10 cm of thread. Add about 5 mL of baking soda.

6. Lower the bag into the bottle taking care not to touch the liquid, and allow the excess thread to hang over the neck of the bottle.

7. Replace the cap so that the bag is left hanging in the bottle.

8. Put a paper clip on the upper end of the straw to reduce its diameter.

9. To activate the device, shake the bottle to wet the bag of baking soda, which will burst.

WHAT'S GOING ON?

The baking soda reacts with the vinegar to produce carbon dioxide gas which creates pressure, forcibly ejecting the water—vinegar—carbon dioxide mixture through the straw.

CANADIAN INFORMATION PROCESSING SOCIETY (CIPS)

WHO WE ARE
We are Canada's largest and oldest organization of Information Technology (IT) professionals. Through initiatives at the national and international level, CIPS strives to strengthen the Canadian IT profession. The membership of CIPS reflects the diversity of the IT field. Members include IT managers, programmers, analysts, system designers, students, consultants, engineers, lawyers, professors and researchers.

Canadian Information Processing Society (CIPS)
Edmonton Section
1230, 10405 Jasper Avenue
Edmonton, AB   T5J 3N4

Tel: (403) 420-6923
Fax: (403) 429-1622

WHAT WE DO
One of our goals is to provide education to the public on computing and related issues. Volunteers will present to youth groups and classrooms upon request.

Programs Offered
Elementary, junior high, high school, youth groups. **Outreach:** *What's Inside a Computer?* and *Information Technology Careers.*

FINGERPRINT DETECTIVE

WHAT YOU NEED

- Glass
- Ink pad
- Paper
- Talcum powder
- Paintbrush (fluffy, wide-tipped)
- Tissue
- Magnifying glass

WHAT TO DO

1. Gather some friends or family members together. Ask one of them to secretly touch a very clean drinking glass in several places while you are out of the room, and leave the glass on a table. You may now return to the room to play detective and find out who touched the glass!
2. Make a record of each "suspect's" fingertips. To do this, you get each person to make a print of each of their fingers. They must first roll their fingers on an ink pad. Then, one at a time, they put the outside edges of their fingers on a piece of paper and roll their fingers in towards their bodies to get a print of a large part of their fingers. They must not press too hard, and roll their fingers gently in one direction.
3. Pick up the used drinking glass with a tissue. Be sure not to get your own fingerprints on the glass.
4. Place the glass on a sheet of paper. Dip the paintbrush into the talcum powder and gently dust one of the fingerprints on the glass. Brush in the direction of the ridges only to reveal the fingerprint pattern.
5. Use a magnifying glass to compare the fingerprints on the glass with those of your friends. Is there a match? Who is the criminal?

WHAT'S GOING ON?

Your fingerprints are unique; they are therefore a good way to identify you. When a person touches an object, a small amount of perspiration and oil from the skin's surface is transferred to the object. Powder sticks to the perspiration and oil and helps to make the prints visible.

WHAT ELSE YOU CAN DO

To keep a fingerprint that you have found, press a piece of clear tape over it. Peel off the tape and check to see that the fingerprint is on it. This is called "lifting" a print. Stick the tape onto shiny black paper.

CANADIAN RED CROSS SOCIETY

WHO WE ARE
We are a charitable organization devoted to promoting health and safety and distributing humanitarian aid.

Canadian Red Cross
Northern Alberta Region, Edmonton Office
9931 - 106 Street
Edmonton, AB   T5K 1E2

Tel: (403) 423-2680
Fax: (403) 428-7092

WHAT WE DO
We provide humanitarian aid and education through programs such as International Services, Blood Services, Emergency Services, Water Safety, and First Aid.

Programs Offered
Elementary, junior high, high school, teacher training, adult, family, community, handicapped, senior citizen, youth groups. **Workshops:** *First Aid, Water Safety, Child Abuse Education.*

Resources
Newsletter, brochures, information sheets.

MOVING ICE

WHAT YOU NEED
- A pan
- Ice cubes
- A toy

WHAT TO DO
1. Half-fill the pan with water. Add enough ice cubes so that the ice appears solid on the top.

2. Place the toy on the ice. Balance it so that it looks "safe".

3. Put your finger in the water at the edge of the pan and move it back and forth.

4. What happens to the toy?

WHAT'S GOING ON?
The ice may look safe and solid but you can see that the "solid" ice isn't really safe at all. Ice on a river or a lake can sometimes look solid even when it isn't. Waves in the water under the ice can make it move just like the ice in the pan.

WHAT ELSE YOU CAN DO
Think about skating on a lake or river. What would you do if you saw a friend in the same situation as your toy?

CHILDREN'S EDUCATIONAL WILDLIFE MUSEUM

WHO WE ARE

We are a museum for children that promotes wildlife appreciation and conservation. We are a non-profit organization and a member of the Alberta Museums Association.

Children's Educational Wildlife Museum
5304 - 97 Street
Edmonton, AB   T6E 5W5

Tel: (403) 434-7462

Days/Hours

By appointment only.

WHAT WE DO

By placing great emphasis on hands-on learning, we provide an excellent opportunity for school children to observe and learn about various animals from around the world. We ensure information regarding habitat and habits is correct by offering conducted tours only. Endangered animals can be observed at the museum, as well as displays of skulls, skins, horns and hair.

Programs Offered

Preschool, elementary, junior high, high school, adult, family, community, handicapped, senior citizen, youth groups. **Tours:** Conducted tours, by appointment only, are arranged for groups of up to 50 children. We are not open to the public.

Facilities

Museum, exhibits and displays, live animals.

WHOSE FEET?

WHAT YOU NEED
- five fingers

WHAT TO DO
1. Take a look at these pictures:

Ape Plantigrade	**Cat** Digitigrade	**Pig** Even-toed ungulate	**Horse** Odd-toed ungulate

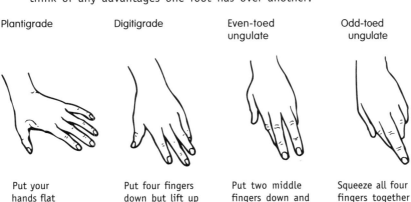

2. Try holding your hands in these positions and imagine how the different animals walk or run. Are there any differences? Can you think of any advantages one foot has over another?

Plantigrade	Digitigrade	Even-toed ungulate	Odd-toed ungulate
Put your hands flat on the table.	Put four fingers down but lift up the heel of your hand.	Put two middle fingers down and pull other fingers behind. Don't let them touch the table.	Squeeze all four fingers together with just the tallest finger touching the table.

WHAT'S GOING ON?
How an animal stands on its feet is an adaptation to the way it lives. Think about how each animal lives and maybe you can figure out why its foot is the shape it is.

CITY ARTS CENTRE

WHO WE ARE
We are a division of the City of Edmonton Parks and Recreation department.

City Arts Centre
Edmonton Parks and Recreation
11507 - 74 Avenue
Edmonton, AB   T6G 0G1

Tel: (403) 496-6955
Fax: (403) 496-7397

WHAT WE DO
We offer a range of programs in the arts and have developed introductory science programs within a recreational context for preschool and elementary students.

Programs Offered
Preschool, elementary, family. **Outreach:** Most of our programs are available on an outreach basis. Please call the office for details. **Summer Camps:** Camps during July and August offer a mixture of arts, science and sporting games. **Workshops/Special Programs:** Programs can be designed to your specifications on request.

Facilities
Classroom, science room.

LEAF PRINTS

WHAT YOU NEED
- Variety of fresh leaves (not dried)
- Ink pad
- Several sheets of paper
- Tweezers

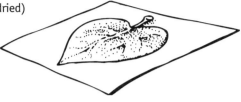

WHAT TO DO
1. Place a leaf, top side up, on to the ink pad.
2. Place a piece of paper over the top of it and press gently.
3. Remove the inky paper and pick up the inky leaf with tweezers.
4. Place the leaf, ink side down, on a clean sheet of paper.
5. Take another sheet of paper and lay it over the leaf.
6. Press the "leaf sandwich" gently all over without moving the leaf.
7. Lift off the upper sheet of paper and remove the leaf with tweezers.
   A leaf print will be on the lower sheet of paper.

WHAT'S GOING ON?
The ridges and soft spots on the underside of the leaf hold the ink in different ways, and transfer the ink to the paper differently. Leaves from different plants will also do this differently, giving you a record of the different types of leaves. Of course, you'll also have a record of the shapes of the leaves.

WHAT ELSE YOU CAN DO
Let the leaf print dry, then label it with the type of plant it came from. Try to gather leaves from many different kinds of plants to make a collection.

CITY OF EDMONTON — WASTE MANAGEMENT

WHO WE ARE
We are a branch of the City of Edmonton Public Works Department.

City of Edmonton
Public Works Department
Waste Management Branch
2nd Floor, Century Place
9803 - 102A Avenue
Edmonton, AB   T5J 3A3

Tel: (403)   496-6544
Fax: (403)   496-5657

WHAT WE DO
We encourage and provide education focusing on the 4 R's: reduce, reuse, recycle and recover.

Programs Offered
Elementary, junior high, high school, adult, and community groups. *Good Planets are Hard to Find* is a puppet show for Grades K to 3 encouraging waste reduction. *Waste and Our World* is a slide show and presentation highlighting the past, present and future of waste management in the City of Edmonton.

Resources
Presentations, slide shows, information sheets, speakers.

Facilities
Compost education centre (located at the John Janzen Nature Centre—see page 112).

COMPOSTING APPLES AND ORANGES

WHAT YOU NEED

- 4 slices of apple or pieces of orange peel
- A clear plastic bag
- Transparent tape
- 2 pickle jars
- Soil
- A large spoon

WHAT TO DO

1. Place two identical slices of apple or orange peel in a clear plastic bag. Tape the bag shut to ensure it remains sealed.
2. Fill the jars with soil and label them 1 and 2. Use the spoon to dig a hole in jar 1, and bury the wrapped fruit.
3. Dig a hole in jar 2. Bury two identical unwrapped pieces.
4. Moisten the soil in both jars with water.
5. Water the jars every other day. Loosen the soil gently with a spoon. Try not to break up the unwrapped fruit or puncture the bag of fruit.
6. Write down what you think will happen to the fruit in the two jars after one week and after two weeks.
7. At the end of the first week, write down what you see in the jars.
8. Carefully scoop out the fruit, leaving the wrapped fruit in the plastic. What changes do you see? Write them down.
9. After you've noted the changes, bury the fruit again.
10. Leave the jars for another week, then write down what you see.

WHAT'S GOING ON?

"Compost" forms when organic matter decays or rots. The decay or decomposition of organic matter is brought about naturally by decomposers like bacteria, fungi, earthworms, and snails, which require oxygen to live. The fruit in the plastic bag simulates the way in which much of our garbage is disposed of—in plastic bags taken to a landfill. Plastic bags slow or stop the break-down process because they prevent oxygen and some decomposers from reaching the organic matter.

WHAT ELSE YOU CAN DO

Try other kinds of fruits and vegetables and note how long each takes to decompose. Try to predict which of them will take the same length of time.

CLIFFORD E. LEE NATURE SANCTUARY

WHO WE ARE
We are a nature sanctuary, owned by the Canadian Nature Federation, dedicated to the conservation and preservation of critical habitats. We are managed by a volunteer committee.

Clifford E. Lee Nature Sanctuary
51306 Range Road 264
Spruce Grove, AB   T7Y 1E7

Tel: (403) 430-7134, (403) 987-4883, or (403) 987-4806

Days/Hours
24 hours a day, 365 days a year.

WHAT WE DO
We provide a natural sanctuary setting for the education and enjoyment of the general public and educational organizations.

Programs Offered
Preschool, elementary, junior high, high school, teacher training, adult, family, community, senior citizen, youth groups. **Field trips:** Field trips and tours can be arranged on request. Group size limited to 30. **Outreach:** When available, guides will go to groups or schools with a slide show and program, for a small fee.

Resources
Slide shows, videos, films, information sheets, portable exhibits.

Facilities
Intrepretive signs, live animals, trails, picnic tables, outhouses.

CRICKET THERMOMETER

WHAT YOU NEED

- Timepiece (wristwatch, stopwatch) that indicates seconds

- Calculator

WHAT TO DO

1. On a summer evening, listen for the chirps of crickets.

2. Try to isolate the chirp of one cricket.

3. Looking at your timepiece, count the number of chirps in 14 seconds.

4. Add 40 to that number and the result will be close to the temperature in degrees Fahrenheit (°F).

5. To find the temperature in degrees Celsius (°C), subtract 32 from the Fahrenheit number, and multiply by five-ninths.

WHAT'S GOING ON?

Insects, like other cold-blooded animals, can move more rapidly in warm weather than in cold, when they are sluggish. Crickets chirp more rapidly as the temperature goes up. Honey bees are so temperature-sensitive that they stay inside their hives when the outside temperature is below 12°C. If you see a bee flying on a winter's day, you'll know that the temperature is at least 12°C.

CROSS CANCER INSTITUTE

WHO WE ARE

The Cross Cancer institute, the comprehensive cancer centre of Northern Alberta, is committed to pursuing excellence in patient care, research and education in an atmosphere of compassion and respect for human dignity.

Cross Cancer Institute
11560 University Avenue
Edmonton, Alberta
T2G 1Z2

Tel: (403) 432-8771
Fax: (403) 432-8411

WHAT WE DO

We engage in innovative research programs ranging from the laboratory to the bedside into the cause, course and control of cancer. Although we do not offer formal education programs, scientists and physicians are available for community classroom visits.

Facilities

The Abdul Khaliq library contains reference materials and periodicals pertaining to the field of cancer. Bookstore/giftshop, cafeteria/snack bar.

IT'S A-PEELING!

WHAT YOU NEED

- Variety of fruit (grapes, apples, oranges, bananas)— two of each type
- Sunscreens with different SPFs
- Cookie sheet
- Paring knife

WHAT TO DO

1. Peel one of each type of fruit.
2. Place all fruit on a cookie sheet.
3. Place cookie sheet in the hot sun for a few hours and leave it undisturbed.
4. Bring the fruit in and carefully remove the peel from the rest of the fruit.
5. Compare it to the fruit that had the peel removed before being placed in the sun. Which looks more healthy and attractive? Is peel important for protecting what's underneath it?

WHAT'S GOING ON?

The fruit with its peel (skin) removed quickly browned or dehydrated in the hot sun. The fruit with its skin intact was fine, even after sitting in the sun for a while. Skin is vital for keeping things healthy. It protects us from disease, regulates our body temperature, and much more, even though it is often taken for granted. We all love a hot, sunny day, but too much of a good thing can be bad! A small amount of sunlight will cause skin cells to tan, but too much sun causes redness, pain and swelling. Over time, exposure to sunlight can result in skin cancer. It is important to protect your skin from the sun's ultraviolet radiation by using high SPF (sun-protection factor) sunscreen whenever you are outside for a long time. Protect your skin because it protects the rest of you!

WHAT ELSE YOU CAN DO

Try different sunscreens on the exposed fruit. Do they protect the tissue?

BE CAREFUL!

Make sure an adult helps if you use a knife to remove the skin. With most fruit, however, you can simply peel the skin off.

DEVONIAN BOTANIC GARDEN

WHO WE ARE
We are a botanic garden, operated by the University of Alberta, and located southwest of Edmonton. We have 16 acres of cultivated plants and 170 acres of sand dunes, sedge fens, mixed-wood forest and other native vegetation.

Devonian Botanic Garden
c/o University of Alberta
Edmonton, AB   T6G 2E1

Tel: (403) 987-2064
Fax: (403) 987-4141

Days and Hours
Call for exact days.

WHAT WE DO
We provide public education on topics such as horticulture and native plant species. We offer an award-winning nature interpretation program for school groups and partially guided tours of our facilities.

Programs Offered
Preschool, elementary, junior high, high school, adult, family, community, senior citizen, youth groups. **Field Trips:** One of our most popular trips is the *Nature Interpretation Program*, suitable for Grades K to 12; class size limited to 50 students. Areas of study within this program include ponds, forest ecology, insects, animal adaptations, environmental quality, Bio 20/30 field study aquatic, Bio 20/30 field study terrestrial. **Summer Camps:** Nature study day camps available for children from 4 to 11 years; dinosaur art and painting classes available for ages 8 to 13 years. **Workshops/Special Programs:** Courses and free slide shows on a broad range of horticultural topics are offered each year. Please call or visit our gardens for further information.

Resources
Books, memberships, presentations, information sheets.

Facilities
Classroom, science room, interpretive/nature centre, butterfly house,

SUFFOCATING LEAVES

WHAT YOU NEED
- 1 house plant (that can afford to lose a few leaves)
- Vaseline

WHAT TO DO
1. Rub Vaseline over the top surface of two leaves.
2. Rub Vaseline over the underside of two other leaves.

WHAT'S GOING ON?
Two of the four test leaves will wither and die because the Vaseline has plugged up the leaves' ability to breathe. Leaves breathe carbon dioxide from the air through little openings on the underside of leaves called *stomata*. Vaseline rubbed over the top side only of the leaves has little effect.

Why do you think plants don't have their stomata on the top side?

DISCOVER E SCIENCE CAMP

WHO WE ARE
We are a not-for-profit science camp, run by engineering students at the University of Alberta. Our motto is: "I hear, and I forget. I see, and I remember. I do, and I understand!".

Discover E Science Camp
Room 5-1, Mechanical Engineering Building
University of Alberta
Edmonton, AB   T6G 2G8

Tel: (403) 433-4471
Fax: (403) 492-0500
E-mail: discover@gpu.srv.ualberta.ca
World Wide Web: http://www.ualberta.ca/~discover/homepage.html

Days/Hours
May and June, 8:30 a.m. to 4:30 p.m.
July and August, 8:00 a.m. to 5:00 p.m.

WHAT WE DO
Through presentations and summer camps, our goal is to show kids that science and engineering are a blast!

Programs Offered
Elementary, junior high school. **Summer Camps:** One-week day camps in July and August focusing on engineering and applied science. Tours of the engineering facilities are held during the camps. **Outreach/Workshops:** In May and June, the Discover E instructors visit schools to give 90-minute presentations on science and engineering.

POP BOTTLE ROCKETS

WHAT YOU NEED
Launcher (see diagram)

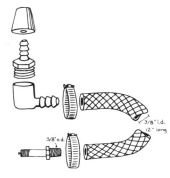

- Wood for L-shaped support
- Rubber stopper with hole
- ½ inch male-thread white nylon hose barb
- ½ inch female thread 90° elbow hose barb
- 12 inch long 3/8 inch o.d. high-pressure tubing
- 2 pipe clamps
- 3/8 inch o.d. inner tube type valve
- Bike pump

Rocket

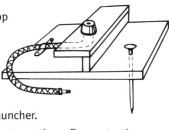

- Two 2-litre pop bottles with one bottle top
- Duct tape
- Corrugated plastic
- Spray paint
- X-acto knife

WHAT TO DO

1. Follow the diagram to build your rocket launcher.

2. Design fins for your rocket on paper. Then trace three fins onto the corrugated cardboard with the X-acto knife.

3. Attach the fins with duct tape, spacing them evenly near the top of one bottle (see diagram).

4. Cut the second bottle in two near the bottom.

5. Place a bottle cap on top of the bottle

6. Place this bottle over the first one and attach the two.

7. Fill the uncut bottle half full of water.

8. Place it over the rubber stopper.

9. Use the bicycle pump to launch your rocket.

WHAT'S GOING ON?
The bicycle pump compresses the air and water, creating a force that pushes the rocket upwards. The fins help keep the rocket stable. You can try experimenting with different amounts of water in the bottle. Or you can vary the design of your rocket, by placing the fins in different places.

BE CAREFUL!
This is a very messy activity—you're going to get wet! It's perfect for doing outside on warm days. You'll need lots of room.

DOW CHEMICAL CANADA INC.

WHO WE ARE
We are a chemical company involved in the research, development and production of chemicals and chemically engineered products, for a wide range of industrial and domestic uses.

Dow Chemical Canada Inc.
Highway 15
Fort Saskatchewan, AB   T8L 2P4

Tel: (403) 998-8476
Fax: (403) 998-8350
World Wide Web: www.dow.com

WHAT WE DO
We educate the public on the role of our industry in society and promote careers in applied science.

Programs Offered
Elementary, junior high, high school. **Tours:** Job-shadowing opportunities for high school students and plant tours for students over 12 years of age. **Outreach:** Our formal school programs include *Partners for Science* and *Partners in Education* (restricted to those jurisdictions where we have partnerships).

Resources
Videos, information sheets.

Facilities
Chemical plant. We also have a *Wildlife Greenbelt* and an *Air Monitoring* exhibit for the public to visit.

INVISIBLE INK

Note: Adult supervision is required for this activity.

WHAT YOU NEED
- Toothpick
- Lemon juice
- White paper
- An iron

WHAT TO DO
1. Soak one end of a toothpick in lemon juice until the tip has softened.
2. Gently write out your message on a sheet of paper, dipping the point in the juice as necessary. (You'll barely be able to read your message even as you write.)
3. Let the ink dry completely.
4. Iron your sheet of paper to bring out the message.

WHAT'S GOING ON?
A chemical change occurs as you apply sufficient heat to the lemon juice. Before the iron has a chance to burn the paper, the heat is able to change the lemon juice to a brown colour, which shows up on your white paper.

WHAT ELSE YOU CAN DO
Try the same thing with milk instead of lemon juice.

BE CAREFUL!
Ask an adult to supervise, as you'll need to use a very hot iron. Remember to unplug the iron after you've finished.

DUCKS UNLIMITED CANADA GREENWING PROGRAM

WHO WE ARE
We are a non-profit organization protecting waterfowl and wildlife habitats today so they may be enjoyed by future generations.

Ducks Unlimited Canada
#202, 10470 - 176 Street
Edmonton, AB   T5S 1L3

Tel: (403) 489-2002
Fax: (403) 489-1856
E-mail: du_edm@duck.ca.
World Wide Web: www.ducks.ca.

WHAT WE DO
We are committed to educating people about the importance of wetlands and the need for their conservation. The Greenwing Program focuses on conveying these messages to young people (17 years and younger) in ways that are interactive and enjoyable. Being involved in hands-on activities increases awareness and appreciation of wetlands and wildlife.

Programs Offered
Preschool, elementary, junior high, family, community, handicapped, youth groups. **Field Trips:** Events are volunteer organized, and are available in various communities throughout Alberta. Call for details in your area. **Summer Camps:** Provincial week-long camp with allocation restrictions; national week-long camp. **Outreach:** *Wetland Environments Unit* school curriculum available for Grade 8.

Resources
Teacher kits, memberships, slide shows, videos, films, magazines, information sheets, posters, collector cards, identification packs, instructional programs.

CREATING A BIRD HABITAT

WHAT YOU NEED
- An old lid or tray
- Some stones
- Water
- Plastic pop bottle with top
- String
- 2 sticks
- Peanuts

WHAT TO DO
1. Build a bird bath from the lid or tray. Make sure the inside is rough, not slippery. Put a few stones in it and make sure to change the water every day.

2. Make two holes near the bottom of the plastic pop bottle. Thread the string through the holes so you can hang the bottle upside down.

3. Draw a line about halfway down the bottle and make ten slits in the bottle from the line to the top.

4. Push the sticks through slots in the bottle to make a perch for the birds.

5. Pour the peanuts into the bottle and hang it upside down.

WHAT'S GOING ON?
Birds often need help to survive through the winter. You can help by building a bird habitat. Birds need food, and water for drinking and bathing. Make a bird habitat and you will be able to see all kinds of birds in your yard.

WHAT ELSE YOU CAN DO
You can build a little "wild area" in your yard. Just put some logs and flat stones around a small area of your yard. Don't plant grass or flowers there, just let it grow wild. It will make a good home for bugs and insects. These will provide good food for birds.

EDMONTON AIRPORTS

WHO WE ARE

Our company manages Edmonton International Airport.

Edmonton Airports
Edmonton International Airport
P.O. Box 9860
Edmonton, AB   T5J 2T2

Tel: (403) 893-8382
Fax: (403) 890-8446

WHAT WE DO

We offer tours that include the main airport terminal building and one additional area: RCMP, Firehall, Canada Customs or the Weather Office. Children get to see the application of science and technology first hand.

Programs Offered

Elementary, junior high, high school, handicapped, senior citizens, youth groups. **Tours:** Call to arrange.

HELI-PAPER

WHAT YOU NEED

- A piece of paper 25 x 5 cm
- A paper clip

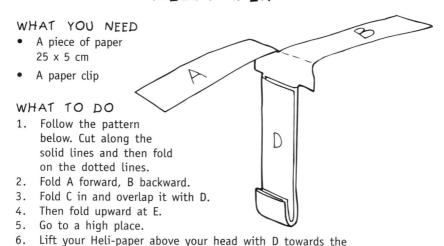

WHAT TO DO

1. Follow the pattern below. Cut along the solid lines and then fold on the dotted lines.
2. Fold A forward, B backward.
3. Fold C in and overlap it with D.
4. Then fold upward at E.
5. Go to a high place.
6. Lift your Heli-paper above your head with D towards the ground, as shown in the diagram, then drop it.

WHAT'S GOING ON?

You have made the type of "wing" used by helicopters. It is called a horizontal rotor. The shape of your rotor causes it to twist due to uneven drag on the paper surface. The rotor begins spinning and this reduces the pressure above the "wing". The pressure underneath the spinning rotor is greater and pushes up, allowing the helicopter to drift slowly down rather than falling quickly. Real helicopters *lift up* when the motor spins the rotor at tremendous speeds.

WHAT ELSE YOU CAN DO

Put a paper clip over the folded part at E. See if it changes the flight pattern.

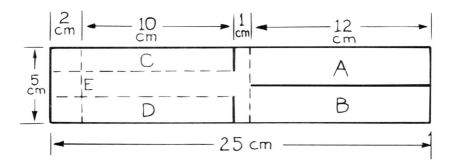

EDMONTON NATURAL HISTORY CLUB

WHO WE ARE

We are an active, diverse group of plant, bird, insect and nature enthusiasts.

Edmonton Natural History Club (ENHC)
Box 1582
Edmonton, AB   T5J 2N9

Tel: c/o Provincial Museum (403) 453-9100

Meeting Place and Time

Field trips to various locations throughout the year. Indoor meetings at the Provincial Museum of Alberta from September through April.

WHAT WE DO

Our members take part in various activities, including the Beaverhill Lake Snow Goose Festival, Christmas bird counts in Edmonton and area, annual banquets, special interest groups. Some members are expert naturalists, whereas others are just discovering the joys of their new hobby.

Programs Offered

Adult, family, community, senior citizens.

FIND THE FOOD

WHAT YOU NEED

- 100 coloured toothpicks, pieces of wool, or pipe cleaners (about 25 of each of four colours). Be sure to include one colour that blends into the activity area, e.g., green for a green lawn.

WHAT TO DO

1. Scatter the coloured toothpicks, wool, or pipe cleaners over an area of about 200 square metres.

2. Ask your friends to play the roles of birds looking for bugs (the coloured objects) to eat. Each person will have a 'nest' where they will collect the coloured objects. The nest will be approximately 25 m from the feeding area.

3. One at a time, the birds (your friends) will run to the feeding area to find food. Each bird takes its turn and makes several flights. Only one bug can be caught per flight. Grab the first food you see.

4. After several flights, how many of each colour of bug has each person collected? What colour of food is the hardest to find? Why?

WHAT'S GOING ON?

Birds don't care what colour worms or insects they eat are, so they grab the first food they see. Birds can't run their hands over the ground, so they pick up bugs only after spotting them. You will notice that the coloured object that is most like the colour of the game area is the hardest food to find. Body colour is a form of adaptation that protects animals by allowing them to blend into their surroundings. This is called "camouflage". When an animal is camouflaged it is harder for its enemies to find. The female of most bird species is dull and drab, which serves as a protection while the bird is nesting. The male bird is often brightly coloured so that it stands out from its environment. In this way, it draws attention away from the nest.

EDMONTON POTATO GROWERS (1971) LTD.

WHO WE ARE
We are a marketing agent with a warehouse for Alberta-grown potatoes and other vegetables.

Edmonton Potato Growers (1971) Ltd.
Box 3847
Edmonton, AB   T5L 4K1

Tel: (403) 447-1860
Fax: (403) 447-1899
World Wide Web: epgpotato@aol.com

Days and Hours
Monday through Friday, 7:00 a.m. to 3:00 p.m.

WHAT WE DO
We wash, grade, package, and market fresh potatoes. We are involved in the warehouse movement of many locally grown fresh vegetables and greenhouse crops.

Programs Offered
Elementary, junior high, high school, youth groups. **Tours:** One-hour tours of our plant are available to children's groups.

THE POTATO PUZZLE

WHAT YOU NEED
- Large potato
- Knife

WHAT TO DO

1. Take your potato and cut it into a square or a rectangle.

2. Make at least one cut across your shape. (It doesn't have to be a straight cut.)

3. Then make one or more cuts from top to bottom. You now have at least four different-shaped pieces.

4. How long does it take your friend(s) to put the puzzle together?

WHAT'S GOING ON?
This activity helps you to think in three dimensions. This is an important skill to develop for problem solving in engineering and science.

EDMONTON POWER

WHO WE ARE

Edmonton Power is an electrical utility company that provides generation and transmission services to Alberta, and distribution services to the City of Edmonton. We also provide electrical inspections, install and manage traffic signals and provide services for the Light Rail Transit, trolley and streetlight systems.

Edmonton Power
10065 Jasper Avenue
Edmonton, AB   T5J 3B1

Tel: (403) 412-3121
Fax: (403) 421-3384
World Wide Web: www.edpower.com

WHAT WE DO

We make an ongoing effort to promote awareness in areas of safety, generation, use and conservation of electricity.

Programs Offered

Elementary, junior high, high school, adult, community, youth groups. **Tours:** For a tour of the gas-fired Clover Bar Generating Station, call 412-3199. **Outreach:** Schools and community groups may book the *ZAPatrol* (high voltage) or the *Hazard Hamlet* safety presentations.

Resources

Teacher kits, videos, presentations, information sheets, student workbooks and posters. Videos on electrical safety include *Zap Rap* (7-12 years), *Volton* (9-12), and *Electrojuice* (9-12). Posters are available for classroom use including: *Play it Safe around Electricity* (Grades 1 to 3) and a set of three for Grades 4 to 9 on the production of electricity. Consumer information is also available on fact sheets or video to assist in buying appliances, microwaving and freezing food, and energy management.

TOGETHER AND APART

WHAT YOU NEED
- 4 balloons
- 4 pieces of nylon string, approximately 60 cm long
- A piece of wool or fur
- Plastic wrap

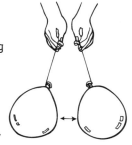

WHAT TO DO
1. Blow up two balloons and tie their necks securely.
2. Tie a piece of string on the neck of each balloon.
3. Rub both balloons with the wool or piece of fur.
4. Hold balloons by their strings, one in each hand.
5. Try to make the balloons touch each other by bringing your hands together. What happens?
6. Blow up the other balloons, tie their necks but this time only rub one balloon with wool or fur.
7. Rub the second balloon with plastic wrap.
8. Try to make the balloons touch each other. What happens this time?

WHAT'S GOING ON?
The balloons are pulled together or pushed apart because of static electricity. Static electricity also causes the shock you get if you touch someone after shuffling across a carpet. Tiny particles called electrons can move from one object to another. When an electron leaves an object, the object has a positive (+) charge. When an electron jumps to an object, the object has a negative (-) charge. When you rub a balloon with the piece of wool or fur, an electron moves from the fur to the balloon. The balloon now has a negative (-) charge. But if you rub a balloon with a piece of plastic wrap, an electron moves to the plastic wrap. The balloon now has a positive (+) charge.

The basic rule of electricity says: Like charges repel each other, or push each other apart; opposite charges attract each other, or pull each other together. When both balloons have the same charge, they push each other apart. When they have different charges they pull each other together. Can you draw in the charges in the illustrations?

WHAT ELSE CAN YOU DO
Turn on the cold water tap in the bathroom so there's a thin stream of water coming from it. Then run a comb through your hair several times. Quickly hold the comb close to the water (don't let it touch the water). Watch the stream of water bend towards the comb.

EDMONTON PUBLIC LIBRARY

WHO WE ARE
We are the second most popular attraction in the city, with over 3.5 million visits a year.

Edmonton Public Library
7 Sir Winston Churchill Square
Edmonton, AB   T5J 2V4

Tel: (403) 496-7055/56
Fax: (403) 496-1885
World Wide Web: http://www.epl.org

WHAT WE DO
We offer a wide range of programs, including *Our Future Scientists Club,* which is offered in various branches.

Programs Offered
Elementary school, adult.

Resources
Books, memberships, presentations, magazines, information sheets, equipment, videos, films, speakers.

Facilities
Auditorium, cafeteria/snack bar, meeting rooms.

CREATING YOUR OWN PAPER

WHAT YOU NEED

- 2 fine nylon screens (20 x 20 cm) in wooden frames
- Construction paper (any colour) and white paper
- Plastic tub approximately 60 cm x 50 cm
- Blender
- Good sponge
- Cornstarch (60 mL per tub)

WHAT TO DO

1. Rip the paper into small pieces (3-5 cm) for the blender.
2. Add water to the blender (three-quarters full), then add the paper.
3. Turn the blender on for approximately 40 seconds to make pulp.
4. Fill the tub with water (three-quarters full).
5. Put the pulp from the blender in the tub.
6. Using the pulpy water in the tub, continue to make more pulp in the blender until the pulp solution is thick (approximately six to seven mixes).
7. Use one of the screens and slowly screen out the pulp.
8. Place the second screen over the pulp in the first screen, and sponge or towel it dry.
9. The pulp should be like paper. Remove it and let it dry.

WHAT'S GOING ON?

It is important to remember that paper comes from trees, which are a precious and limited resource. Fortunately, paper is easily recycled, which is what you did in this actvity. You have removed the original paper (wood) fibres from the used sheets, and then reformed them into usuable paper again. If you use a magnifier, you can actually see the tiny wood fibres and feel their texture with your fingers. The fibres from which paper is made can be recycled into many other things, including boxes, wallboard, and even tissue for your nose! Most importantly, for every tonne of paper that is recycled, you save 17 trees!

WHAT ELSE YOU CAN DO?

Try making different colours of paper, or adding sparkles to it for gift wrap.

EDMONTON REGIONAL SCIENCE FAIR

WHO WE ARE
We are the volunteer organization that conducts the Edmonton Regional Science Fair each year. We raise funds and secure judges and prizes.

Edmonton Regional Science Fair
c/o Thomas Sherwood
4724 - 144 Street
Edmonton, AB   T6H 4G8

Tel: (403) 462-7954
Fax: (403) 461-1841

WHAT WE DO
We promote participation in science by children in Grade 3 and up and encourage the public to view and discuss the projects with the young participants.

Programs Offered
Public viewing of science fair projects.   Watch local media for this year's dates.

THE GREAT EGG SHELL DISAPPEARANCE

WHAT YOU NEED

- A glass jar
- A hard-boiled egg
- 250 mL vinegar

WHAT TO DO

1. Place the egg in the jar.
2. Cover the egg with vinegar.
3. Make a note of what you see.
4. Check in 24 hours to see if anything has happened.

WHAT'S GOING ON?

The bubbles that increasingly form on the egg are carbon dioxide gas. With the acetic acid present in vinegar and the calcium carbonate present in the egg shell, a chemical reaction occurs causing the egg shell to disappear.

WHAT ELSE YOU CAN DO

Chalk is also made up of calcium carbonate. Try placing chalk in the vinegar. What do you think will happen?

EDMONTON REPTILE AND AMPHIBIAN SOCIETY

WHO WE ARE
We are a society of people interested in all areas of herpetology, the branch of zoology dealing with reptiles and amphibians.

Edmonton Reptile and Amphibian Society
P.O. Box 52128, 8210 - 109 Street
Edmonton, AB   T6G 2T5

Tel: (403) 462-8167
Fax: (403) 492-1617
World Wide Web: www.ualberta.ca/~rswan/ERAAS/

Meeting Place and Time
Every third Tuesday of each month.

WHAT WE DO
We further the members' interest in reptiles and amphibians through monthly meetings and in our bimonthly newsletters. Although we don't offer any formal educational programs, society members are available for classroom visits. The society also maintains a library of herpetological-related books and journals.

Programs Offered
Adults, family, community.

BEAN SNAKE

WHAT YOU NEED

- Construction paper
- White glue
- Pencil
- Dried beans (e.g., kidney, lentil, split peas)
- A coloured picture of a snake

WHAT TO DO

1. Find a picture of a snake that you like.

2. On the construction paper draw a picture of the snake that you want to make.

3. Find the beans that match the colour of the snake. For example, use kidney beans if you need a red colour or lentils if you need a green colour.

4. Using the white glue, glue the beans onto the construction paper in the right places so that the colours match the picture of the snake.

5. Let everything dry overnight.

6. Start all over again with a new picture.

WHAT'S GOING ON?

When choosing the picture of the snake, you want to find information on where the snake lives and what type of habitat it lives in. Does the colour of the snake allow it to hide from predators or the animals it preys on? If not, what other purpose could the colours have? Do they warn other animals of danger?

WHAT ELSE YOU CAN DO

You can also try this with pictures of lizards or frogs.

EDMONTON SCIENCE AND TECHNOLOGY HOTLINE

WHO WE ARE

We are a service agency designed to promote awareness of science, engineering and technology, particularly among elementary, junior and senior high school students.

Edmonton Science and Technology Hotline
10129 - 143 Street
Edmonton, AB   T5N 2R8

Tel: (403) 448-0055
Fax: (403) 453-2711
E-mail: hotline@oanet.com

WHAT WE DO

Our co-ordinator responds to requests for: information, answers to a puzzling science question, a speaker or demonstrator, science fair judge or job-shadow partner, by contacting a volunteer with expertise in the area of interest.   We also co-ordinate Industry Canada's *Innovators in the Schools* programs.

Programs Offered

Preschool, elementary, junior high, high school, teacher training, community, senior citizens, youth groups. **Outreach:** Speakers often bring hands-on activities or materials to accompany their presentations.

Resources

Speakers, scientist/teacher workshops.

BOILING WATER WITH AN ICE CUBE

Note: Adult supervision is required for this activity.

WHAT YOU NEED

- Empty baby food jar
- Kettle or hot plate to boil water
- Oven mitts
- Ice cube

WHAT TO DO

1. Boil some water.

2. Place the jar on an oven mitt to insulate it from the counter top. Fill the jar two-thirds full with boiling water and seal tightly.

3. Observe the water. Is it boiling? How do you know?

4. Put an ice cube on top of the lid.

5. Observe the water. What happens?

WHAT'S GOING ON?

When water boils, the bubbles we see are water vapour leaving its liquid state and going into the air above the water. Air takes up less space when it is cooled. In the airtight jar, the ice cube cools the air above the just-boiled water and creates a partial vacuum. This means there is lower air pressure in the space between the water and the lid. With lower air pressure directly above the just-boiled water, some of the water will leave its liquid state to become water vapour. In other words, the water boils (even though the water is not as hot as when it first boiled).

WHAT ELSE YOU CAN DO

Can you think of other places where water boils at a temperature of less than 100°C (the normal boiling point of water). The activity showed us that water boiling temperature varies, depending on air pressure. At sea level, water boils at 100°C. However, in Alberta, where the air pressure is lower because we are hundreds of metres above sea level, water boils at slightly below 100°C.

BE CAREFUL!

Boiling water has enough energy to cause burns! Use your oven mitts.

EDMONTON SPACE & SCIENCE CENTRE

WHO WE ARE
We are a unique facility dedicated to inspiring a greater appreciation of science and technology.

Edmonton Space & Science Centre
11211 - 142 Street
Edmonton, AB   T5M 4A1

Tel: (403) 452-9100
Fax: (403) 455-5882
Booking Office: (403) 451-3344
E-mail: essc@planet.eon.net

Days and Hours
Open daily at 10:00 a.m.   Closed Mondays except holidays.

WHAT WE DO
We focus on providing opportunities for the community to explore the world and beyond, in an educational and entertaining manner. We offer an IMAX® Theatre, Canada's largest planetarium dome, exciting exhibit galleries, the first international Challenger Learning Centre, an observatory, and the Dow computer lab.

Programs Offered
Preschool, elementary, junior high, high school, teacher training, adult, family, community, handicapped, senior citizens, youth groups. Astronomy courses and astronomy badge courses for Brownies, Cubs and Guides, and computer courses from beginner to advanced for all ages. **Outreach:** *Science in Motion*, a program led by one of our science interpreters, may be booked in advance.   Groups may rent an inflatable planetarium if unable to come to the centre. **Summer Camps:** *Science Adventure Camps* and *Children's Computer Camps* run during the summer. **Special Programs:** Adult extension courses on astronomy; *Challenger Learning Centre* program.

Resources
Books, memberships, inflatable planetarium, information sheets.

Facilities
Auditorium, exhibits, displays, classroom, science room, book and giftshop, cafeteria/snack bar, observatory, Dow Computer Lab, Margaret Zeidler Star Theatre, IMAX® Theatre.

ROUND AND ROUND
THE PLANETS GO

WHAT YOU NEED
- A sharp pencil
- A ruler
- A big piece of paper
- A compass

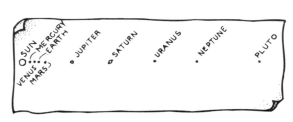

WHAT TO DO
1. At one end of your big piece of paper mark a spot. This is where you will draw the sun. Earth is 149.6 million kilometres from the sun. This is called one astronomical unit or 1 A.U.

SUN ⟷ EARTH

2. Make 1 A.U. equal to 1 cm. Now you can make a scale drawing of the solar system.

3. The distances of the planets are:

Mercury	0.4 A.U.
Venus	0.7 A.U.
Earth	1.0 A.U.
Mars	1.5 A.U.
Jupiter	5.2 A.U.
Saturn	9.6 A.U.
Uranus	19.3 A.U.
Neptune	30.3 A.U.
Pluto	40.0 A.U.

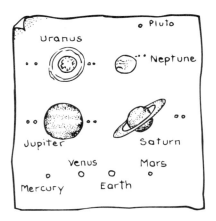

4. Mark the distance each planet is from the sun on your paper.

5. Label each planet.

WHAT ELSE YOU CAN DO
Use a compass to make a scale drawing of the planets and colour them in. Shrink the Earth to 1 cm. Then the other planets are:

Mercury	2 mm	Venus	1 cm
Earth	1 cm	Mars	5 mm
Jupiter	11 cm	Saturn	9 cm
(minus the rings)		Uranus	4 cm
Neptune	4 cm	Pluto	2 mm

EDMONTON SYMPHONY ORCHESTRA

WHO WE ARE
Established in 1952, we are a 56-member professional group of musicians that brings world class entertainment to Edmonton and surrounding areas.

Edmonton Symphony Orchestra
10160 - 103 Street
Edmonton, AB   T5J 0X6

Tel: (403) 428-1108
Fax: (403) 425-0167
Toll Free: 1-800-563-5081
E-mail: eso@oanet.com
World Wide Web: www.ctqx.com/eso

WHAT WE DO
We at the Edmonton Symphony are dedicated to creating beautiful music—enhancing the reputation of our city and enriching the lives of everyone in our community.

Programs Offered
Elementary, junior high, high school, adult, family, community, handicapped, senior citizens. **Concerts:** Our education concerts are designed to introduce school children and youths to the joys of symphonic music. All concerts feature a diverse repertoire around one theme and are targeted to three age groups: Grades 1 to 3, Grades 4 to 6 and Grades 7 to 12.

Resources
Compact disc recordings

Facilities
Auditorium, bookstore/giftshop, cafeteria/snack bar.

MAKING WIND INSTRUMENTS

WHAT YOU NEED

- Old garden hose
- Funnel
- Scissors
- Many glass pop bottles
- Water

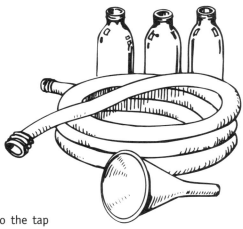

WHAT TO DO

French Horn

1. Place the funnel in the cut-off end of the hose.
2. Coil the hose in the shape of a French Horn.
3. Buzz your lips and blow into the tap attachment end of the hose.
4. Cut the hose to raise the pitch.

Caruba Tube

1. Hold the end of the hose and swing it quickly in the air to produce a pitch.
2. Cut the end of the hose to raise the pitch.

Wind Orchestra

1. Line up the bottles and fill them with water, from a few drops in the first one to a full bottle for the last one.
2. Blow across the top of the bottles, as you would with a flute, and create tunes with different pitches.

WHAT'S GOING ON?

In an orchestra, musicians make air vibrate to produce musical notes in three main ways—with strings, pipes or by hitting a surface. In a wind instrument, like the ones in this activity, the note depends on the length of the pipe and the materials it is made from.

WHAT ELSE YOU CAN DO

Try making some stringed instruments, like the cake pan guitar on page 111. What else can you use to make a stringed instrument? What could you use to make instruments like the drums or xylophone in an orchestra, where notes are produced by hitting a surface?

ELK ISLAND NATIONAL PARK

WHO WE ARE
We are a national park dedicated to preserving
our natural and cultural heritage.

Elk Island National Park
Site 4, R.R. 1
Fort Saskatchewan, AB   T8L 2N7

Tel: (403) 992-2959
Fax: (403) 992-2951

Days and Hours
Varies throughout the season. Please call in advance.

WHAT WE DO
By offering a variety of different programs to all age groups, we are able to
educate the public on subjects such as pond study, ecology, native
culture, trees and forests, various animals and their habitats.

Programs Offered
Elementary, junior high, high school, post-secondary credit, teacher training,
adult, family, community, handicapped, senior citizen, youth groups. **Field
Trips:** Numerous field trips available, brochures in French or English, please
phone for further details. **School Programs:** Various programs for Grades K to
12. All programs connect with school science curricula. All programs use
hands-on, on-site activities, giving the opportunity to explore ecological
inter-relationships, population and communities, and animal adaptation and
behaviour.

Resources
Presentations.

Facilities
Interpretive/nature centre, live animals, trails, cafeteria/snack bar, theatre.

LITTER CRITTERS

WHAT YOU NEED
- 1 funnel
- 1 glass jar
- Black construction paper
- Desk lamp
- Pile of freshly gathered leaf litter
- Masking tape

WHAT TO DO
1. Wrap glass jar in black paper and secure with tape.
2. Place funnel in jar opening.
3. Place leaf litter in funnel.
4. Shine lamp over leaf litter.

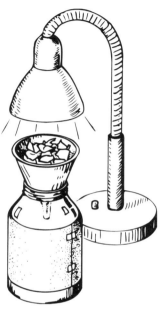

WHAT'S GOING ON?
Tiny critters live in the litter layer on the forest floor. After an hour or so, check to see if any litter layer creatures have fallen into the jar. Why would the animals move out of their litter layer (too hot or too light)? Describe the animals you see and maybe group them according to the number of legs or how they move.

Remember—when you have finished looking at the animals, put them back into the wild!

ENERGY EFFICIENCY ASSOCIATION OF ALBERTA

WHO WE ARE

We are a not-for-profit organization that promotes energy efficiency and resource conservation.

Energy Efficiency Association of Alberta
P.O. Box 41152
Edmonton, AB   T6J 6M7

Tel: (403) 448-0035
Fax: (403) 463-2360

WHAT WE DO

We provide educational information to elementary students, focusing on energy resources, energy conservation, and energy and the environment.

Programs Offered
Preschool, elementary.

Resources
Teacher kits (includes a teacher's guide, student materials and a poster).

HOT FOOT

WHAT YOU NEED

- A warm day
- Pair of socks

WHAT TO DO

1. Soak one sock in water.
2. Put the socks on your feet (one wet and one dry) and lie in the sun. Which foot is warmer?

WHAT'S GOING ON?

Water from the wet sock is evaporating. Evaporation uses energy. Heat is one kind of energy, and the heat from your foot is being used to evaporate water from the wet sock. That's why that foot feels cooler.

WHAT ELSE YOU CAN DO

On a hot day, put one foot on tiles and one on a carpet. Which feels cooler? With a thermometer, check whether the temperature of the tiles is different from the temperature of the carpet.

ENVIRONMENT CANADA

WHO WE ARE

We are a department of the federal government concerned with the preservation of Canada's natural environment and wildlife.

Environment Canada
Prairie and Northern Region
200, 4999 - 98 Avenue
Edmonton, AB   T6B 2X3

Tel: (403) 951-8717
Fax: (403) 495-2478
World Wide Web *(Green Lane)*: http://www.ec.go.ca

WHAT WE DO

At Environment Canada, our goal is a Canada where people make responsible decisions about the environment so that the environment is sustained for the benefit of present and future generations. We provide educational materials to teachers and the general public.

Resources
Brochures, fact sheets and materials offered for the general public.

Facilities
Library.

MEASURING RAINFALL

WHAT YOU NEED

- Tin can, open at the top, with no lip, so you can pour the rainwater out of it easily.

- Wood to make a platform. (A log or a box with a flat top, stuck into the ground, will do.)

- Ruler

- Tall narrow glass jar

- Grease pencil or paint

WHAT TO DO

1. Make a stand on which to place the tin can and jar. The top of the can should be level and about 30 cm above the ground.

2. Using a ruler to measure, pour water into the can to a depth of one centimetre. Pour this water into the tall jar. Mark the water level with a grease pencil or paint. This will be the mark for 1 cm of rain. From this first mark you can measure and mark tenths of centimetres all the way to the top of the jar.

3. Position the rain can as far away as possible from buildings, trees, fences, or other objects that might interfere with the rain catch. After rainfall, pour rain from the can into the jar. Read off rainfall in centimetres and tenths of centimetres (millimetres). Read at least once a day, or preferably, twice a day at regular times. Note your observations.

4. Graph the results over a period of time to see what trend emerges.

WHAT'S GOING ON?

An instrument for collecting and measuring rainfall is called a rain gauge. You have made a simple one.

WHAT ELSE YOU CAN DO

You can measure snowfall in the winter. Leave your rain gauge out. Let it fill up with snow and note how many centimetres of snow you have. Then, take it inside and let it melt. Note how many centimetres of melted snow you have. What happened? The difference between the amount of snow and water (melted snow), is how much air was in the snow.

FEESA

WHO WE ARE

We are a society providing Alberta educators with access to a wide variety of environmental educational resources. All our programs are supported by industry, government and private foundations.

FEESA
An Environmental Education Society
900, 10150 - 100 Street
Edmonton, AB   T5J 0P6

Tel: (403) 421-1497
Fax: (403) 425-4506

WHAT WE DO

We educate and assist Alberta educators in making real-world connections to topics and issues that relate to the ecosystem that sustains our society and the economy that supports it. We provide bias-balanced resources, offer workshops and institutes for teachers, and network with other agencies to help provide teachers with local resources to enhance their teaching.

Programs Offered

Post-secondary credit, teacher training, community.
Field Trips: Several field-based eight-day *Institutes* for teachers and community educators as well as two and three-day, field-based *Ecotours*.
Workshops: *Ecolabs* are one-day workshops covering such topics as waste, weather, and wetlands; geared to upper elementary teachers. Topics vary from year to year for Institutes, Ecotours, and Ecolabs.

Resources

Teacher kits, memberships, video presentations, films, magazines.

BUILDING YOUR OWN WATERSHED

WHAT YOU NEED

- Regular-size shoebox with removable lid
- 20 small, blue, see-through plastic or glass beads
- 20 pieces of fishing line (10 cm each)
- Small stones, cones of different shapes and sizes
- Plasticine, play dough or felt pieces (blue, green, brown)
- Construction paper (green, brown)
- Glow-in-the-dark star or fluorescent stickers
- Glue, scissors

WHAT TO DO

1. Cut out two round holes (the size of a dollar coin), side by side, in one of the short sides of the box.

2. Put the lid on and punch holes in it with your pencil (at least 60).

3. Tie a blue bead at the end of each fishing line, loop the other end through two holes in the lid and tie off on the inside of the lid.

4. Create a lake (use Plasticine, felt, paper, etc.) at the bottom of your box. Have a river flowing out of it, place rocks at the lake shore to make a dam, glue cones to create a forest, make trees and animals out of Plasticine.

5. Out of construction paper, cut out mountains and glue them to the inside sides of the box; stick stars above the mountains.

6. Put the lid on and look inside!

WHAT'S GOING ON?

The forests, people, the fish, the water, and wildlife are all connected through our watersheds. You have created a model of a watershed. As the rain falls on the land, it collects in a man-made lake called a "reservoir". From here, underground pipes carry water to your home. This is the place where your drinking water comes from. The forest is an important part of the watershed; it filters the air and the water and provides homes for the animals. Forests give us many things to make our environment healthy. They also provide us with trees, from which we can make many things.

4-H FOUNDATION OF ALBERTA

WHO WE ARE

The 4-H Foundation of Alberta is a charitable organization that runs a camp facility at Battle Lake. The camp is used as a provincial training centre for 4-H youth, but is also available to non-4-H members.

4-H Foundation of Alberta
Alberta 4-H Centre
Highway 13 West, RR 1
Loesterose, AB   T0C 2V0

Tel: (403) 682-2153
Fax: (403) 682-3784
E-mail: bigmac@ccinet.ab.ca

WHAT WE DO

We offer an environmental appreciation program for Grade 4 to 6 students. The Alberta 4-H Centre has over 143 acres of well preserved lake-front property featuring some unique species of flora and fauna. The Grant MacEwan Environmental Centre, featuring hands-on interactive learning stations and an environmental library, is also available for rent.

Programs Offered

Elementary, junior high school. Complete instruction for groups is available.

Resources

Books, videos, films, portable exhibits.

Facilities

Auditorium, exhibits and displays, classroom, cafeteria/snack bar, library, dormitory, self-guided trail, lake. The facility may be rented by groups wishing to do their own programming.

MAKING OLD-FASHIONED PAINT FROM MILK

WHAT YOU NEED

- Water
- Non-fat, dry milk powder
- Colouring materials, like coloured chalk ground into powder, berry juice (strawberry or cherry), beet juice, or coloured earth

WHAT TO DO

1. Mix the powdered milk and water in a large container. Use a 1:1 proportion (e.g., 250 mL water to 250 mL milk powder). You should get a thick, paint-like liquid. If the liquid is too thick, add more water. If it is too thin, add more milk.

2. Add the colouring material to the liquid. Add more for an intense colour, less for a paler shade.

3. Use your milk paint to paint a picture.

WHAT'S GOING ON?

Paint is used to colour and protect objects from weather and use. In the old days, farmers did not have access to the same kind of paint we use today. To protect their barns, homes and furniture, they used paint made from things easily found around their farms, namely milk, berry juices, and coloured earth.

IMAGINATION MARKET ASSOCIATION OF ALBERTA

WHO WE ARE
We are a non-profit association promoting the value of reuse.

Imagination Market Association of Alberta
#8, 10510 - 121 Street
Edmonton, AB   T5N 1L4

Tel: (403) 413-9326
Fax: (403) 488-6974

WHAT WE DO
We promote public awareness and education on reclaiming, reducing and reusing materials traditionally seen as waste. We provide industries with a waste management alternative that promotes reuse before recycling.

Programs Offered
Preschool, elementary, teacher training, adults.
Workshops: We conduct hands-on creative workshops for all ages. We also have *Festival* workshops, *Adult Permission to Play* workshops, and classroom workshops within schools.

Resources
Teacher kits, memberships, information sheets, materials.

Facilities
Classroom, workshop, on-site store.

CAKE PAN GUITAR

WHAT YOU NEED
- Metal cake pan
- Elastic bands
- Paper
- Tape

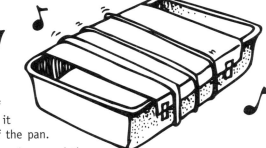

WHAT TO DO
1. Tape a piece of paper across the top of the cake pan, securing it firmly to the outside of the pan.
2. Stretch several rubber bands around the cake pan side-by-side, as illustrated. The rubber bands should be of different thickness andstretched different amounts (i.e., some can be doubled or even tripled over to make them tighter).
3. Place the cake pan on a table and hold the paper down with one finger to keep it away from the rubber bands. Now gently pluck the rubber bands with the other hand.

WHAT'S GOING ON?
As you pluck the rubber bands, they will vibrate very quickly. They cause the air to vibrate, producing sound waves of different pitch. The variations in rubber band thickness and tightness will produce different sounds because they vibrate at different rates (i.e., different frequencies). The paper acts like a simple amplifier and starts to vibrate at the same frequency as the plucked rubber band.

WHAT ELSE YOU CAN DO
Arrange the rubber bands in order of pitch, from lowest to highest. What happens if you remove the paper or try to stretch the rubber bands at right angles to the paper?

Try using a glass cake pan—does it work as well as the metal pan? Try making other musical instruments (see page 99).

JOHN JANZEN NATURE CENTRE

WHO WE ARE
We are a nature preservation and interpretation centre operated by Edmonton Parks and Recreation for the education and enjoyment of the citizens of Edmonton.

John Janzen Nature Centre
Edmonton Parks and Recreation
P.O. Box 2359
Edmonton, AB   T5J 2R7

Tel: (403) 496-2939
Fax: (403) 496-4701

Days and Hours
Hours vary by season.

WHAT WE DO
We bring natural history to life with fun, interactive programs and exhibits.

Programs Offered
Preschool, elementary, junior high, adult, family, community, handicapped, senior citizen, youth groups. **Field Trips:** Hands-on fun for preschoolers and early elementary students—*Super Sleuths, Dinosaur Adventures* and *Peter Rabbit's Birthday*. Curriculum-based programs for upper elementary students, such as *Pond Adventure*. *Rocks* and *River* badge-based programs for Guiders. **Outreach:** Curriculum-based programs for school classes—*Owls, Dinosaurs* and *Seasonal Discovery*. **Summer Camps:** *Chickadee Kids* and *Treehouse Gang* will delight preschool and elementary children. *Careers in Conservation* attracts teens preparing to make important choices.

Resources
Books, teacher kits, memberships, information sheets.

Facilities
Auditorium, exhibits and displays, interpretive/nature centre, live animals, trails, bookstore/giftshop.

FALL COLOURS

WHAT YOU NEED
- A fresh, green leaf
- A coin
- A strip cut from coffee filter paper
- Rubbing alcohol
- Tall, slim glass jar

WHAT TO DO
1. Place the filter paper on the table.
2. Put the leaf on top of one end of the filter paper.
3. Roll the edge of the coin back and forth over the leaf so that a green line of leaf material is left across the filter paper about 3 cm from the tip.
4. Allow the leaf material to dry on the filter paper.
5. Pour enough rubbing alcohol in your jar to cover the bottom 2 cm.
6. Suspend the tip of the filter paper into the alcohol so that the green line is about 1 cm above the level of the alcohol.
7. Watch what happens as the alcohol travels up the filter paper past the green line.

WHAT'S GOING ON?
Using this colour separation method (known as chromatography), you'll find that there are different chemicals in the leaf, each with its own colour. During the growing season, leaves look green because there is more chlorophyll present than any other chemical. In fall, chlorophyll breaks down first, allowing the other chemicals in the leaf to show their colours. Each species of plant has different amounts of the coloured chemicals in the leaves. For example, the Sugar Maple leaf (represented on the Canadian flag) has more red chemicals than some other varieties of maple.

WHAT ELSE YOU CAN DO
Repeat this with the leaves of various trees. If you already know what colour their leaves change to in the fall, compare this knowledge with the colours that turn up on your filter paper. Try it again with leaves from a tree that you don't know and try to predict what colours its leaves will turn next fall.

BE CAREFUL!
Rubbing alcohol is poisonous! Return it to a safe place. It is also flammable (can catch on fire), so keep it away from flames.

NORTHERN ALBERTA WILDERNESS ASSOCIATION

WHO WE ARE
We are the Edmonton chapter of the Alberta Wilderness Association. We are the largest group in Western Canada working to protect wildlands.

Northern Alberta Wilderness Association
10020 - 82 Avenue
Edmonton, AB   T6E 1Z3
Tel: (403) 439-8744
Fax: (403) 413-0698

WHAT WE DO
We promote sound ideas for conserving wilderness, do research, publish books and other literature, sponsor workshops and conferences and work with government and industry to encourage careful management of our natural lands and wild rivers.

Programs Offered
Elementary and high school, adult.

Resources
Newsletter, memberships, presentations, slide shows, videos, films.

Facilities
Library, bookstore/giftshop.

MAKING A WATER'S EDGE VIEW TANK

WHAT YOU NEED
- A large clear plastic container with a wide neck
- A sketchpad or notepad

WHAT TO DO
The next time you're at the beach or by a river or lake, you'll be able to study water creatures for the day when you build your own view tank.

1. Put your container on a flat surface.

2. Put some sand on the bottom of the container as well as some pebbles, seaweed or other plants.

3. Fill the container with sea water, river water or lake water, depending on where you are.

4. Catch small water creatures and put them in your view tank.

5. Make notes and sketches of the creatures. What do they look like? What colour are they? What kinds of things are they doing in the tank?

6. Study them for the day as much as you want, then let them go at the end of the day.

7. Rinse out your view tank at the edge of the water before taking the empty tank home.

WHAT ELSE YOU CAN DO
When you get home, see if you can find pictures of the creatures in your nature books. If not, consult some library books at school or your local library. Take the notes and sketches you made with you. Can you identify the creatures that were with you for the day?

BE CAREFUL!
Make sure you don't try to catch creatures that might hurt you. Ask an adult to help you.

PROVINCIAL MUSEUM OF ALBERTA

WHO WE ARE

We are a museum facility, established in 1967, that houses major collections representing Alberta's cultural and natural history.

Provincial Museum of Alberta
12845 - 102 Avenue
Edmonton, AB   T5N 0M6

Tel: (403) 453-9100
Bookings: (403) 453-9131
Fax: (403) 454-6629
World Wide Web: www.pma.edmonton.ab.ca

Days and Hours

Call for information on times, admission fees, and group accommodation.

WHAT WE DO

We display exhibits and artifacts representing the history of the land, nature and people of the province of Alberta. We offer public education programs and tours to interpret these displays.

Programs Offered

Preschool, elementary, junior high, high school, family, youth groups, handicapped. Call the booking office for specific details on science programs for students K to Grade 12. Specialized gallery tours, workshops and outreach programs also available upon request.

Resources

Books, newsletter, memberships, audio tours.

Facilities

Auditorium, museum, exhibits and displays, live animals, bookstore and giftshop, cafeteria/snack bar, lecture room, lunch rooms.

FIZZY ROCKS

WHAT YOU NEED
- Vinegar
- Variety of rocks
- Spoon or medicine dropper

WHAT TO DO
1. Use fairly clean and dry rocks. Drop a bit of vinegar from a spoon or medicine dropper on to a rock surface. Some rocks will fizz quickly, some slowly, and some not at all.

2. If you have trouble noticing the fizzing, put your ear very close to the rock with the vinegar and listen.

WHAT'S GOING ON?
Vinegar is a weak acid. When acid comes in contact with a material called carbonate, a chemical reaction occurs, which releases bubbles of carbon dioxide gas. The sound of thousands of these tiny bubbles popping is the fizzing you can hear. Rocks that do not contain any carbonate will not fizz.

WHAT ELSE YOU CAN DO
Geologists use a similar acid test when they are in the field, to help determine what kind of rock they are examining. Limestone and dolomite are examples of carbonate rocks common in some areas. Sandstone does not usually contain much carbonate, but sometimes has a naturally occurring carbonate cement or carbonate coating (a white crust) that may produce a fizz. Test your rocks in the field and make a note of where you find the fizzy ones.

REYNOLDS MUSEUM

WHO WE ARE
We are a private, not-for-profit museum displaying antique tractors, steam engines, cars, trucks, aircraft and military vehicles.

Reynolds Museum
4110 - 57 Street
Wetaskiwin, AB   T9A 2B6

Tel: (403) 352-6201
Fax: (403) 352-4666

Days and Hours
Open daily May 15 through Labour Day, 10:00 a.m. to 5:00 p.m.

WHAT WE DO
We restore and display vintage airplanes, vehicles and artifacts. Visitors to our museum can see how the science and technology of transporation have developed over the years.

Programs Offered
Tours: Self-conducted walking tours.

Facilities
Museum, exhibits and displays.

POP CAN PORSCHE

WHAT YOU NEED

- Pop can
- Hammer
- Nail
- Rubber bands
- Pencil
- Plastic bead
- Plastic disk (cut from an ice cream container)
- Wire (bent coat hanger)
- Popsicle stick

WHAT TO DO

1. Using a hammer and nail, make a hole in the bottom of a pop can. The hole must be big enough for a rubber band to pass through.

2. Cut a plastic disk (from an ice cream bucket or lid) to fit the top of a pop can. Poke a hole through the centre of this disk.

3. Thread the rubber band through a plastic bead then through the centre of the disk. Loop it over a pencil so it doesn't pull back through the bead.

4. Using a long wire hook, pull the rubber band through the top of the pop can and out the bottom. Loop this end of the rubber band over a Popsicle stick so that it cannot be pulled back into the can. (The stick must be broken so that its length is less than the can's diameter.)

5. Wind the pencil around until the rubber band is tight. Set the Pop Can Porsche on the floor so that as the pencil tries to unwind it pushes on the floor.

6. Release and watch your Pop Can Porsche roll away. If it slips and spins on the floor, wrap rubber bands outside the can to act as tires.

WHAT'S GOING ON?

As the rubber band unwinds, it tries to turn the Popsicle stick and the pencil. The friction between the Popsicle stick and the can is too great to move the stick. The pencil can move because the bead and plastic disk have less friction between them. However, when the pencil tries to turn, it pushes on the floor (which pushes back) and the only way the rubber band can unwind is to roll the can forward. As the can rolls, the potential energy that is stored in the wound rubber band is transformed into motion (kinetic energy) and heat. The can will roll if the energy stored in the wound rubber band produces a force great enough to overcome the force of friction between the bead and the disk, and the can and the floor.

ROYAL ASTRONOMICAL SOCIETY OF CANADA

WHO WE ARE
We are a society of individuals interested in astronomy and in promoting the astronomical sciences.

Royal Astronomical Society of Canada (R.A.S.C.)
c/o President
#430-51112 Range Road 222
Sherwood Park, AB   T8C 1G9
OR
Royal Astronomical Society of Canada (R.A.S.C.)—Edmonton Centre
c/o Edmonton Space & Science Centre
11211 - 142 Street
Edmonton, AB   T5M 4A1

Tel: (403) 922-4021
Fax: (403) 455-5882
World Wide Web: http://worldgate.com/~rasc/

Meeting Place and Time
Second Monday each month (except July and August), 7:30 to 9:30 p.m. at the Edmonton Space and Science Centre.

WHAT WE DO
We promote an interest in astronomy among R.A.S.C. members and the general public. During Astronomy Week, held in spring, members set up telescopes at the Edmonton Space & Science Centre and other locations around the city to promote astronomy. During special astronomical events, members set up telescopes for public viewing of the event. Regular night observing sessions are held at the Waskehegan Staging Area or the Blackfoot Integrated Use Area, south of Highway 16, near Elk Island National Park, during weekends near the time of new moon. Call for times. Public invited.

Programs Offered
Elementary, junior high, high school, adult, community, youth groups.
Workshops: *Alberta Star Party* held once a year; *Alberta Workshop* held once every two years. **Outreach:** Speakers will visit classes and other groups to present talks or telescope observing sessions.

Resources
R.A.S.C. memberships, telescope rentals.

STAR OR PLANET?

WHAT YOU NEED
- Sheet of paper
- Pencil

WHAT TO DO
1. Draw a star map of a group of stars in the sky where you suspect that one of the bright stars might be a planet.

2. Two weeks later, go out and look for the same group of stars.

3. Draw the position of your suspected planet onto the same map.

4. In another two weeks, draw in the "planet's" position on your map.

WHAT'S GOING ON?
If your suspected planet is still in the same place near its neighbouring stars, it too is a star. However, if it has moved a little, it's a planet.

WHAT ELSE YOU CAN DO
Can you find any other planets? Look at your planet through binoculars or a telescope.

SCIENCE ALBERTA FOUNDATION

WHO WE ARE

We are a non-profit organization dedicated to promoting science literacy throughout Alberta. Our mission is to create and inspire innovative programs that will encourage Albertans to discover and share the excitement and relevance of science. We receive our core funding from the Alberta Lottery Fund, with additional funding from corporate donations. Our programs are made possible through the many partnerships formed with corporations, businesses, teachers, librarians, individuals, and communities.

Science Alberta Foundation
1200, 800 - 6th Avenue S.W.
Calgary, Alberta   T2P 3G3

Tel: (403) 260-1996
Fax: (403) 260-1165
E-mail: litebulb@saf.ab.ca
World Wide Web: www.freenet.calgary.ab.ca/saf/

WHAT WE DO

With a vision of creating centres for science in every Alberta community, we provide a variety of quality programs—hands-on science and technology workshops, summer institutes, travelling exhibitions, Science in a Crate, publications and special projects. Our exhibitions and activities are portable, flexible and accessible, for shipping throughout the province. We also support the Science Hotlines in Calgary, Edmonton, Medicine Hat and Peace River Country (Grande Prairie).

Programs Offered

Preschool, elementary, junior and senior high school, post-secondary, teacher and librarian training, parents, family, community, senior citizen, youth groups.

Resources (some fees apply)

Newsletter, travelling exhibitions, Science in a Crate, and publications: *Integrating Computers in the Classroom; Best of the Web; Let's Do Science; Science Begins at Home; Backyard Safari; Ready, Set Science - Weather* and *Crawly Critters* activity guides.

RAINBOW MILK

WHAT YOU NEED

- Foil or glass pie plate
- Homogenized milk
- White fluted coffee filter
- Food colouring (red, yellow, blue)
- Dishwashing liquid soap (Sunlight works well)

WHAT TO DO

1. Pour some milk into the pie plate until it covers the bottom and is about 1 cm deep.

2. Add some drops of food colouring randomly.

3. Swirl very slowly with something like a pencil or the tip of a spoon. Try not to mix the colours too much. What new colours are appearing?

4. To make a print of the pattern in the milk, you can lower a white fluted coffee filter gently onto the surface of the milk. Lift it up, then turn it over to dry.

5. Put a few drops of dishwashing liquid soap into a small container, or onto a piece of waxed paper. Add one drop of soap from there into the milk mixture. Add another drop of soap or some more colour if the swirling slows down.

WHAT'S GOING ON?

What do you see happening? What words can you describe it with? What does it remind you of? The primary colours mix to make secondary colours. The soap interferes with the surface tension of the milk, and also affects the fat in the milk.

WHAT ELSE YOU CAN DO

Test different kinds of milk and water. What differences do you see between skim milk and homogenized milk? Hint: the higher the fat content in the milk, the better the experiment works.

SHUSWAP ASSOCIATION FOR THE PROMOTION OF ECOLOGICAL DEVELOPMENT

WHO WE ARE

We are a volunteer charitable organization established in 1989 to help link the concerns of ecological sustainability with community development.

Shuswap Association for the Promotion of Ecological Development (SAPED)
14703 - 66 Avenue
Edmonton, AB   T6H 1Z1

WHAT WE DO

We do extensive work in Central America, supporting a large number of ecological development projects such as reforestation, organic agriculture, soil erosion control, and energy and natural resource conservation. In Canada we co-ordinate events to increase awareness about ecological issues, sustainable lifestyles and the ecological and social links between Canadians and our neighbours in the South.

Programs Offered

Elementary, junior high, high school, post-secondary, adult. Speakers available to visit schools. Opportunities for post-secondary students and adults to volunteer in Central America to learn about ecological development issues.

Resources

Newsletter, memberships, presentations, slide shows, videos, films, speakers.

MAKING YOUR OWN WATER CYCLE

WHAT YOU NEED

- Commercial-size mayonnaise jar with screw-on lid
- Small stones
- Sand
- Potting soil
- Small plants such as mosses, ivy, baby ferns or other plants found in the woods
- A shell or large bottle cap
- Water

WHAT TO DO

1. Layer the following in the bottom of the jar: stones, 1 cm deep; sand, to cover stones; soil, about 10 cm deep.
2. Create a nice arrangement for the plants and bury the roots in the soil.
3. Fill the shell or cap with water to create a lake in the terrarium.
4. Tightly screw the lid on the terrarium.
5. Keep the terrarium in a shady place and watch what happens over the next few days.

WHAT'S GOING ON?

The water from the lake in the terrarium evaporates, then condenses on the lid. It falls back down into the soil and lake, and the water cycle starts all over again.

SOLAR ENERGY SOCIETY

WHO WE ARE
We are a local chapter of a national organization dedicated to the science and employment of solar energy.

Solar Energy Society
Northern Alberta Chapter
10020 Whyte Avenue
Edmonton, AB   T6E 1Z3

Tel: (403) 439-5608
Fax: (403) 413-0698

Meeting Place and Time
Varies—speakers four to six times a year, annual general meeting in May.

WHAT WE DO
We are devoted to helping others use the sun's energy directly. We display at community fairs, distribute educational materials and speak to groups on the use of solar energy. *Solar Drive Car and Inventor* kits are available for children ages 9 to 13.

Programs Offered
Elementary, junior high. We are currently developing a resource package for the Grade 9 solar energy unit. **Outreach:** Class visits for all grade levels, can be arranged on request.

Resources
Books, newsletter, teacher kits, memberships, presentations, speakers,

A SOLAR WATER CLEANER

WHAT YOU NEED

- Large bowl
- Drinking glass
- Stones
- Small amount of dirt
- Clear plastic wrap
- Water

WHAT TO DO

1. Mix a small amount of dirt into about 1 litre of water.
2. Pour the dirty water into a bowl.
3. Stand a glass in the centre of the bowl.
4. Cover the bowl with clear plastic wrap and weigh down the edges of the plastic with stones.
5. Place a stone on the plastic over the centre of the glass.
6. Leave the water cleaner in the sun all day.
7. Remove the plastic. Look in the glass. What do you see?

WHAT'S GOING ON?

Clean water evaporates from the dirty water. It condenses on the plastic and collects in the glass.

STRATHCONA NATURAL HISTORY GROUP

WHO WE ARE
We are a family oriented subgroup of the Edmonton Natural History Club (see p. 82). Our goal is to increase knowledge and appreciation of all aspects of natural history, including mosses, lichens, trees, bushes, mammals, birds, insects, amphibians, clouds and rainbows.

Strathcona Natural History Group
Box 146
Ardrossan, AB   T8E 2A1

Tel: (403) 922-6675
Fax: (403) 427-3462

Meeting Place and Time
Third Saturday of each month from September to June, 9:00 a.m. to noon.

WHAT WE DO
We offer half-day guided walks, hikes and canoe trips and participate in other nature programs in partnership with Strathcona County Parks and Recreation.

Programs Offered
Elementary, adult, family, youth groups. **Field Trips:** Half-day guided walks, hikes, canoe trips. **Outreach:** Nature programs. **Workshops/Special Programs:** Strathcona Christmas bird count.

BAT HAVEN

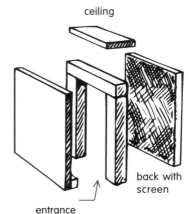

ceiling

back with screen

entrance

WHAT YOU NEED

- Staples or glue

- Black paint or stain

- Wood, any kind, new or used:
  - 1 piece of lumber or plywood for the front and back
  - 1 piece of 2.5 cm x 5 cm lumber for the ceiling and walls
  - 1 piece of 2.5 cm x 10 cm lumber for the roof

- 1 piece of fibreglass window screening, same dimensions as the back wall of the bat house

- A helpful adult

WHAT TO DO

1. With the help of an adult, cut the first piece of wood into pieces about 35 cm x 55 cm for the front and back. The front should be about 2 cm shorter than the back.

2. Attach a strip of wood to the bottom inside of the front. This makes the entrance to the bat house smaller so that no other animals can get in. This entrance should be 2 cm (from the front inside to the back).

3. Staple the fibreglass screen to the inside of the back of the house. This makes a good place for the bats to hold onto.

4. Cut the 2.5 cm x 5 cm piece of wood into three pieces—one for the ceiling and two for the side walls.

5. Glue or nail the house together, then stain or paint it.

6. The house is small inside—5 cm front to back—and the bottom is open.

WHERE TO PUT IT

Mount it facing south on a tall pole or tree, or the south side of a building—the sunnier the better. Put it near open water if you can, where there are lots of insects (bat food). Make sure there are no obstructions underneath.

BE PATIENT

It will take some time before bats actually use the house.

STRATHCONA WILDERNESS CENTRE

WHO WE ARE

We are a unique centre consisting of 550 acres of forested public parkland on the shores of Bennett Lake. The centre offers a wide range of outdoor recreational experiences in a natural setting.

Strathcona Wilderness Centre
Strathcona County, Recreation, Parks and Culture
c/o 2025 Oak Street
Sherwood Park, AB   T8A 0W9

Tel: (403) 922-3939
Fax: (403) 922-6415

Days and Hours

Park hours vary. Call for hours.

WHAT WE DO

We offer environmental and outdoor education programs developed to accommodate students, youth groups, families, hikers, skiers and nature buffs. A wide variety of residential lodge and group campsite accommodation is available. We offer full cross-country ski services, including 12 km of groomed trails, rental equipment and lessons. We have hiking trails, a natural interpretive trail, camping and picnic sites, and canoe rentals, spring through fall.

Programs Offered

Preschool, elementary, junior high, high school, teacher training, adult, family, community, handicapped, senior citizen, youth groups. **Workshops/ Special Programs:** A wide variety of programs are available for every age group, including campfire program, predator/prey survival game, canoeing, kayaking, orienteering, outdoor skills, cross-country skiing, *Nature Detective* programs. Teen outdoor recreation and leadership programs throughout the year. **Summer Camps:** Camps available for ages 5 through 18, including day and overnight camps featuring nature hikes, canoeing, outdoor cooking, swamp walks, shelter building, mountain biking, and much more.

Resources

Books, activity kits, information sheets, equipment.

ANIMAL FRIGHT DISTANCE

WHAT YOU NEED
- Rocks or pieces of cloth to use as markers
- Paper
- Pencil or pen

WHAT TO DO
1. Go for a walk. When you see an animal, such as a squirrel or a raccoon, note its exact location. (If you find a landmark such as a tree or a big rock it will help you remember the location.)

2. Walk slowly toward the animal while holding the marker in your hand. When the animal moves away from you, drop the marker.

3. Pace out the distance between the marker and where the animal was, just before it moved or ran away. This is the "fright distance". Record the fright distance and the type of animal you saw.

4. Find the average fright distance for a particular type of animal.

5. Compare the fright distance of various types of animals.

WHAT'S GOING ON?
You can tell the difference between tame and wild animals by how easily they are frightened. For example, birds are very timid creatures. Sudden or quick movements cause them to take flight. A bird will allow you to get only so close and then it will fly away. Some birds tend to be more timid than others. Fright distance varies with the type of bird and whether or not a bird is used to having human beings around.

TELEPHONE HISTORICAL CENTRE

WHO WE ARE
We are a non-profit foundation, supported in part by Telus, featuring a specialized communications science centre.

Telephone Historical Centre
10437 - 83 Avenue
Edmonton, AB   T6E 4T5

Tel: (403) 441-2077
Fax: (403) 433-4068
E-mail: thc@planet.eon.net
World Wide Web: www.discoveredmonton.com/telephonemuseum

Days and Hours
Monday through Friday, 10:00 a.m. to 4:00 p.m.; Saturday, 12:00 p.m. to 4:00 p.m.; Sundays, closed.

WHAT WE DO
We have numerous hands-on displays that demonstrate communication principles. Edmonton's history is presented through a multi-media show emphasizing telecommunications.

Programs Offered
Preschool, elementary, family, community, handicapped, senior citizens.
Tours: Guided and audio tours available. **Outreach:** *Hello Central* is a slide presentation on the history of the telephone combined with a travelling exhibit of antique telephones. **Workshops/Special Programs:** School programs connected with science and social studies for kindergarten and elementary students include *Amazing Magnets, Fun with Sound, Light Fantastic, Electrifying Encounters, Community Connections* and *Telephone Connections*.

Resources
Books, teacher kits, memberships, presentations, slide shows, equipment, audio tours, archives.

Facilities
Auditorium, museum, exhibits and displays, classroom, library, bookstore/giftshop.

STRING TELEPHONE

WHAT YOU NEED
- 2 paper cups
- Some string
- 2 paper clips
- A pencil
- Scissors
- A friend

WHAT TO DO
1. Make a small hole in the middle of the bottom of each paper cup by gently poking it with the pencil point.
2. Cut a piece of string about one metre long.
3. Thread the string through the holes in the cup.
4. Tie the ends of the string around the paper clips.
5. Talk into one cup while your friend listens at the other end of your string telephone.

WHAT'S GOING ON?
The sound from your voice makes the string vibrate. The sound vibrations travel along the string to the other cup—and you can hear your friend talk.

WHAT ELSE YOU CAN DO
See if your sound vibrations work better with tight or loose strings. See if you can feel the vibrations in the cup or the string. Can you join string from several cups to make a conference call?

TROUT UNLIMITED CANADA

WHO WE ARE
We are a private, non-profit, charitable organization dedicated to the conservation and wise use of our trout and other cold-water fisheries and their watersheds, through habitat restoration and enhancement, research, management and public education. We co-sponsor the Yellow Fish Road Program with the City of Edmonton.

Trout Unlimited Canada
The Yellow Fish Road Program, Edmonton
c/o The City of Edmonton
Transportation Department, Drainage Branch
Century Place, 6th Floor
9803 - 102A Avenue
Edmonton, AB   T3J 3A3

Tel: (403) 496-3474
Fax: (403) 496-5648

WHAT WE DO
Through the Yellow Fish Road Storm Drain Marking Program, we educate the public about the dangers of indiscriminate dumping of hazardous household waste. The project involves youth groups, such as Girl Guides, and school groups, who paint yellow fish beside storm drains on city streets. Appropriate literature, delivered on a fish-shaped door hangar, is distributed to neighborhood homes to educate the public on the preservation of our waterways.

Programs Offered
Preschool, elementary, junior high, adult, family, community, handicapped, youth groups. **Outreach:** Presentations to groups, including a video, encourages participation in the program.

Resources
Presentations, videos, display board.

OIL AND WATER

WHAT YOU NEED

- 2 clear glasses or jars
- A few drops of vegetable oil
- A spoon
- Fake fur, fabric scraps, feathers, or stones (at least 2 of each)

WHAT TO DO

1. Fill each container with equal amounts of water.
2. Add a few drops of oil to one container.
3. Stir the oil and water and let them sit for twenty minutes. What has happened to the oil?
4. Dip each of the objects into the water; one into the oily water and one into the other water.
5. Observe the objects after you have dipped them.

WHAT'S GOING ON?

Oil is less dense than water so it forms a layer on top of the water. Oil polluting our rivers, lakes and oceans does the same thing. It covers objects the same way your dipped objects were covered.

WHAT ELSE YOU CAN DO

1. Try cleaning up the objects with paper towels and water.
2. Try "booming" the oil—collecting the oil by skimming the surface using Popsicle sticks or a spoon.
3. Try cleaning the oil with cotton balls.
4. Add a few drops of detergent—what happens?

THINGS TO THINK ABOUT

What does oil do to our water and to the fish and other creatures that live in it? What happens to the birds that swim and dive in the water? What about wildlife and people who drink the water? Which clean-up methods would be safe? What can people do to keep the water clean in the first place?

UNIVERSITY OF ALBERTA
DEPARTMENT OF PHYSICS

WHO WE ARE
We are the Department of Physics, University of Alberta.

University of Alberta
Department of Physics
Edmonton, AB   T6G 2J1

Tel: (403) 492-5286
Fax: (403) 492-0714
World Wide Web: www.phys.ualberta.ca

Thursday evenings during the university's academic year (except exam times). Other times available upon request. Please call to confirm.

WHAT WE DO
We focus mainly on astronomy and have a program run by volunteer undergraduate students. They make use of the astronomical observatory on campus in their programs for public groups.

Programs Offered
Elementary, junior high, high school, post-secondary credit, teacher training, adult, family, community, senior citizens, youth groups. **Tours:** Observing the sun, moon, planets, stars. **Workshops/Special Programs:** Special programs have been prepared for Scouts, Beavers, Brownies and Guides.

Resources
Astronomical displays and presentations, slide shows, videos, films, lectures.

Facilities
Observatory on roof of Physics building, telescopes.

HOW BIG IS THAT MOON?

WHAT YOU NEED
- A tube 60 to 80 cm long
- A clear night with a full moon

WHAT TO DO

1. Go outside and look at the moon at two different times. Once when it is just above the horizon and once when it is high in the sky. Is the moon the same size both times?

2. Also look at the moon through your long tube. Does it look the same or different?

WHAT'S GOING ON?

The moon actually doesn't change size during the night. But when it is close to the horizon we compare it to the things that are on the horizon and it looks very big. However, when we look at it through the tube we can't see anything around it. It then looks the same whether it is close to the horizon or high in the sky.

VALLEY ZOO

WHO WE ARE
We promote the conservation, rehabilitation and propagation of exotic and endangered animals. Our displays educate the public on the need for preservation of wildlife and their habitats.

Valley Zoo
P.O. Box 2359
Edmonton, AB   T5J 2R7

Tel: (403) 496-6911
Fax: (403) 944-7529

Days and Hours
Open daily year-round. Hours vary by season.

WHAT WE DO
We provide visitors with a quality educational and recreational experience through exhibit displays and interpretation of exotic and endangered animals.

Programs Offered
Preschool, elementary, junior high, high school, adult, family, community, handicapped, senior citizen, youth groups. **Field Trips:** Curriculum-based fun! Live animals included in almost every program. Choose from a number of options from *Animal Discovery* to *Seasonal Changes*. **Tours:** Self-guided tour kits available as well as guided tours. **Outreach:** Travelling zoo can visit your classroom or any meeting place. **Summer Camps:** *Zoo Kids Club, Kinderzoo Camp* and *Art Safari* are just a few ways children can explore the world of wildlife.

Resources
Teacher kits, memberships.

Facilities
Bookstore/giftshop, cafeteria/snack bar.

CREATING A BETTER SCAVENGER

WHAT YOU NEED
- Collection of household items (e.g., toothpicks, string, wire, elastic bands, glue, tape, stirring sticks)
- Scavenger food challenge materials (e.g., raw eggs, small Styrofoam ball in a cup, plastic bag with 4 kg of sand, dry leaves, bowl of wet noodles covered with plastic wrap, popcorn kernels, tapioca, rice)

WHAT TO DO
1. Think about the animals that scavenge things in your area. How do crows and ravens eat "road kill"? How do coyotes feed off a carcass? Think about how scavengers eat something that is already dead.

2. Set up three (or more if you like) of the following scavenging simulations, using the scavenger "food":
   - carcass or food scrap to pick up (e.g., bag filled with sand or leaves)
   - carcass with meat and organs (e.g., covered bowl of noodles)
   - carcass to be hidden underground for a later feast
   - fragile food morsel to be carried to safety
   - slippery, oil-rich fish eggs to be picked up and eaten

3. Using the household items, create "animal" body parts that will be able to perform scavenging tasks.

4. Test the "body parts" on make-believe carcasses and food items. Try testing different food items and body parts.

5. Note the body parts that worked best. Why were they useful? What real animal body parts do they compare to? Think about your favourite and least favourite animals. What body adaptations do they have for survival?

WHAT'S GOING ON?
By trying out different body adaptations, you can figure out how bio-mechanics works for scavengers. Bio-mechanics is the study of energy and forces and their effect on living bodies. The more efficient the bio-mechanics, the easier it is for a scavenger to get its next meal.

SCIENCE AND NATURE RESOURCES

CLUBS AND SOCIETIES

PROFESSIONAL ORGANIZATIONS

PROFESSIONAL ORGANIZATIONS (CONT'D)

FACILITIES

HANDS-ON ACTIVITIES

HANDS-ON ACTIVITIES (CONT'D)

ALBERTA EDUCATION SCIENCE CURRICULUM LINKS

GRADE 1
- Creating Colours, 89, 109, 111, 123
- Seasonal Changes, 61, 65, 79, 113
- Building Things, 33, 37, 47
- Senses, 13, 21, 41, 49, 69, 71, 83, 103
- Needs of Animals and Plants, 11, 23, 29, 73, 75, 79, 85, 93, 131, 133

GRADE 2
- Exploring Liquids, 25, 61, 89, 109, 111, 123, 129, 135
- Buoyancy and Boats, 35
- Magnetism, 87
- Hot and Cold Temperatures, 45, 55, 69, 103
- Small Crawling and Flying Creatures, 7, 9, 51, 69, 71, 83, 85, 101, 141

GRADE 3
- Rocks and Minerals, 7, 15, 43, 67, 117
- Building With a Variety of Materials, 33, 47
- Testing Building Materials and Designs, 141
- Hearing and Sound, 33, 47, 71
- Animal Life Cycles, 9, 115

GRADE 4
- Waste and Our World, 7, 43, 89, 127, 129
- Wheels and Levers, 37
- Building Devices and Vehicles that Move, 37, 119
- Light and Shadows, 23, 59, 137
- Plant Growth and Changes, 17, 65, 73, 75, 113

GRADE 5
- Electricity and Magnetism, 39, 87
- Mechanisms Using Electricity, 41
- Classroom Chemistry, 13, 15, 25, 49, 55, 57, 77, 91, 117
- Weather Watch, 35, 61, 69, 71, 95, 103, 105, 107, 125, 127
- Wetland Ecosystem, 7, 11, 19, 31, 45, 63, 115, 141

DID WE MISS YOU?

If you would like to be included in the next *Edmonton Science Fun Guide*, please fill in the form below, mail or fax it to Bare Bones Publishing, and we'll send you a questionnaire.

Name of Organization:

_____

Name of Contact Person:

_____

Mailing Address:

_____

_____

Postal Code:

_____

Telephone:

_____

Fax:

_____

Mail completed form to Bare Bones Publishing, Suite 355, 305-4625 Varsity Drive N.W., Calgary, Alberta T3A 0Z9, or fax to (403) 239-0563.

Science Fun Guides

Calgary Science Fun Guide (2nd edn.)

Compiled for the Calgary Science Network, the Calgary Science Fun Guide is the ideal reference for exploring science and nature in Calgary. Containing over 60 hands-on activities, it's the perfect book for budding scientists and their parents, teachers and group leaders.

ISBN 1-896865-02-X $14.95   160 p   softcover

Edmonton Science Fun Guide

An A to Z of where to go and what to do in Edmonton if your passion is science or nature. A superb source of over 60 neat hands-on activities that will open your eyes to the wonderful worlds of science, technology and nature.

ISBN 1-896865-00-3 $14.95   160 p   softcover

Greater Vancouver Science Fun Guide

The Greater Vancouver Science Fun Guide is full of places to go, clubs to join, and lots of things to see and do. It lists key organizations in the Lower Mainland involved in science and nature . . . from beekeeping to playing music in the symphony orchestra! This terrific resource guide puts you in touch with over 70 groups offering science experiences. Includes over 70 hands-on activities.

ISBN 0-9696095-9-0 $12.95   160 p   softcover

South Vancouver Island Earth Science Fun Guide

For all rock hounds and other earth science buffs! This comprehensive guide to South Vancouver Island's earth science resources is a must for visitors as well as locals. It contains essential information on over 50 clubs, organizations and facilities, as well as unique hands-on activities, written by local earth scientists.

ISBN 1-896865-01-1 $10.95   112 p   softcover

See order form on page 151

ORDER FORM

To order any of the Science Fun Guides on page 150, please fill in the form below and mail it with your payment to Bare Bones Publishing.

Name:

_____

Mailing Address:

_____

_____

_____

Postal Code:

_____

Telephone:

_____

Copies:

_____	_Calgary Science Fun Guide_ @ $14.95	$ _____
_____	_Edmonton Science Fun Guide_ @ $14.95	$ _____
_____	_Greater Vancouver Science Fun Guide_ @ $12.95	$ _____
_____	_South Vancouver Island Earth Science Fun Guide_ @ $10.95	$ _____
	Shipping and handling @ $2.00 per copy	$ _____
	Subtotal	$ _____
	G.S.T. @ 7%	$ _____
	Total	$ _____

Please send cheque or money order to Bare Bones Publishing, Suite 355, 305-4625 Varsity Dr. N.W., Calgary, Alberta T3A 0Z9 Tel: (403) 239-7555 or 1-800-852-3335; Fax: (403) 239-0563.

Total $		Mastercard ☐	Cheque ☐
Card Number			
Expiry Date	M Y	Signature	